Student Solutions Manual

Robert Arnold

CALIFORNIA STATE UNIVERSITY - FRESNO

Excursions in
Modern Mathematics

Third Edition

Peter Tannenbaum

Robert Arnold

Prentice Hall, Upper Saddle River, NJ 07458

Acquisitions Editor: Sally Denlow
Production Editor: Barbara Kraemer
Special Projects Manager: Barbara A. Murray
Supplement Cover Manager: Paul Gourhan
Supplement Cover Designer: PM Workshop Inc.
Supplement Editor: April Thrower
Manufacturing Buyer: Alan Fischer

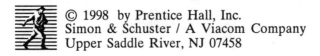
Printed in the United States of America

10 9 8 7 6 5 4 3 2 1

ISBN 0-13-746967-5

Prentice Hall International (UK) Limited, *London*
Prentice Hall of Australia Pty. Limited, *Sydney*
Prentice Hall Canada, Inc., *London*
Prentice Hall Hispanoamericana, S.A., *Mexico*
Prentice Hall of India Private Limited, *New Delhi*
Prentice Hall of Japan, Inc., *Tokyo*
Simon & Schuster Asia Pte. Ltd., *Singapore*
Editora Prentice-Hall do Brazil, Ltda., *Rio de Janeiro*

Contents

Chapter 1: The Mathematics of Voting

Walking

1. **(a)**

Number of voters	5	3	1	3
1st choice	*A*	*C*	*B*	*C*
2nd choice	*B*	*B*	*D*	*B*
3rd choice	*C*	*B*	*C*	*D*
4th choice	*D*	*D*	*A*	*A*

   (b) No

   There are 12 votes altogether, so a majority winner would have to have at least 7 votes.

   (c) The Country Cookery (*C*)

   A has 5 first-place votes, *B* has 1 first-place vote, *C* has 6 first-place votes, and *D* has no first-place votes, so *C* is the winner of the election using the plurality method.

   (d) Blair's Kitchen (*B*)

   A has $4 \times 5 + 3 \times 0 + 2 \times 3 + 1 \times 4 = 30$ points; *B* has $4 \times 1 + 3 \times 11 + 2 \times 0 + 1 \times 0 = 37$ points; *C* has $4 \times 6 + 3 \times 0 + 2 \times 6 + 1 \times 0 = 36$ points; *D* has $4 \times 0 + 3 \times 1 + 2 \times 3 + 1 \times 8 = 17$ points.

3. **(a)** 55

   $3 + 4 + 9 + 9 + 3 + 5 + 8 + 2 + 12 = 55$

   (b) *B*

   A has 16 first-place votes, *B* has 17 first-place votes, *C* has 10 first-place votes, and *D* has 12 first-place votes.

5. *D*

   Round 1. *A*: 16; *B*: 17; *C*: 10; *D*: 12. Eliminate *C*.
   Round 2. *A*: 18; *B*: 17; *D*: 20. Eliminate *B*.
   Round 3. *A*: 26; *D*: 29. *D* wins.

7. *C*

   A has $5 \times 8 + 4 \times 0 + 3 \times 0 + 2 \times 7 + 1 \times 6 = 60$ points; *B* has $5 \times 3 + 4 \times 5 + 3 \times 8 + 2 \times 0 + 1 \times 5 = 64$ points; *C* has $5 \times 5 + 4 \times 5 + 3 \times 5 + 2 \times 6 + 1 \times 0 = 72$ points; *D* has $5 \times 5 + 4 \times 3 + 3 \times 8 + 2 \times 5 + 1 \times 0 = 71$ points; *E* has $5 \times 0 + 4 \times 8 + 3 \times 0 + 2 \times 3 + 1 \times 10 = 48$ points.

9. Winner: *D*. Second place: *A*. Third place: *C*. Fourth place: *B*. Last place: *E*.

   Round 1. *A*: 8; *B*: 3; *C*: 5; *D*: 5; *E*: 0. Eliminate *E* so *E* is in last place.
   Round 2. *A*: 8; *B*: 3; *C*: 5; *D*: 5. Eliminate *B* so *B* is in fourth place.
   Round 3. *A*: 8; *C*: 5; *D*: 8. Eliminate *C* so *C* is in third place.
   Round 4. *A*: 8; *D*: 13. *D* wins and so *A* is in second place.

11. Winner: *D*. Second place: *B* and *C* (tied). Last place: *A* and *E* (tied).

   A versus *B* (13 to 8): *A* wins; *A* versus *C* (8 to 13): *C* wins; *A* versus *D* (8 to 13): *D* wins; *A* versus *E* (10 to 11): *E* wins; *B* versus *C* (11 to 10): *B* wins; *B* versus *D* (8 to 13): *D* wins; *B* versus *E* (16 to 5): *B* wins; *C* versus *D* (10 to 11): *D* wins; *C* versus *E* (18 to 3): *C* wins; *D* versus *E* (13 to 8): *D* wins. 1 point for *A*; 2 points for *B*; 2 points for *C*; 4 points for *D*; 1 point for *E*.

13. **(a)**

Number of voters	5	3	5	5	3
1st choice	A	A	C	D	B
2nd choice	B	D	D	C	D
3rd choice	C	B	A	B	C
4th choice	D	C	B	A	A

(b) D

A has $4 \times 8 + 3 \times 0 + 2 \times 5 + 1 \times 8 = 50$ points; B has $4 \times 3 + 3 \times 5 + 2 \times 8 + 1 \times 5 = 48$ points; C has $4 \times 5 + 3 \times 5 + 2 \times 8 + 1 \times 3 = 54$ points; D has $4 \times 5 + 3 \times 11 + 2 \times 0 + 1 \times 5 = 58$ points.

15. R

Round 1. C: 15; H: 45; O: 0; R: 40; S: 0. Eliminate O, S.
Round 2. C: 15; H: 45; R: 40. Eliminate C.
Round 3. H: 45; R: 55. R wins.

17. Winner: H. Second place: R. Third place: C. Last place: O, S (tied).

C: 15; H: 45; O: 0; R: 40; S: 0.

19. Winner: O. Second place: C. Third place: H. Fourth place: R. Last place: S.

C has $5 \times 15 + 4 \times 40 + 3 \times 0 + 2 \times 45 + 1 \times 0 = 325$ points; H has $5 \times 45 + 4 \times 0 + 3 \times 0 + 2 \times 0 + 1 \times 55 = 280$ points; O has $5 \times 0 + 4 \times 60 + 3 \times 40 + 2 \times 0 + 1 \times 0 = 360$ points; R has $5 \times 40 + 4 \times 0 + 3 \times 0 + 2 \times 15 + 1 \times 45 = 275$ points; S has $5 \times 0 + 4 \times 0 + 3 \times 60 + 2 \times 40 + 1 \times 0 = 260$ points.

21. **(a)** B

A has $5 \times 8 + 4 \times 3 + 3 \times 7 + 2 \times 0 + 1 \times 6 = 79$ points; B has $5 \times 0 + 4 \times 21 + 3 \times 2 + 2 \times 1 + 1 \times 0 = 92$ points; C has $5 \times 2 + 4 \times 0 + 3 \times 8 + 2 \times 13 + 1 \times 1 = 61$ points; D has $5 \times 13 + 4 \times 0 + 3 \times 1 + 2 \times 10 + 1 \times 0 = 88$ points; E has $5 \times 1 + 4 \times 0 + 3 \times 6 + 2 \times 0 + 1 \times 17 = 40$ points.

(b) Yes. D has a majority (13) of the first-place votes but does not win the election.

23. Winner: D. Second place: A. Third place: C. Fourth place: E. Last place: B.

A: 8; B: 0; C: 2; D: 13; E: 1.

25. Winner: A. Second place: B and C (tied). Last place: D and E (tied).

A versus B (12 to 11): A wins; A versus C (12 to 11): A wins; A versus D (12 to 11): A wins; A versus E (13 to 10): A wins; B versus C (6 to 17): C wins; B versus D (14 to 9): B wins; B versus E (16 to 7): B wins; C versus D (15 to 8): C wins; C versus E (11 to 12): E wins; D versus E (16 to 7): D wins. 4 points for A; 2 points for B; 2 points for C; 1 point for D; 1 point for E.

27. **(a)** Winner: E. Second place: C. Third place: A. Fourth place: D. Last place: B.

Round 1. A: 5; B: 0; C: 8; D: 3; E: 7. Eliminate B so B is in last place.
Round 2. A: 5; C: 8; D: 3; E: 7. Eliminate D so D is in fourth place.
Round 3. A: 5; C: 11; E: 7. Eliminate A so A is in third place.
Round 4. C: 11; E: 12. E wins and so C is in second place.

(b) Yes. A is a Condorcet candidate but did not win the election.

A versus B (12 to 11): A wins; A versus C (12 to 11): A wins; A versus D (12 to 11): A wins; A versus E (13 to 10): A wins.

29.   **(a)**   *A*

           A has $4 \times 12 + 3 \times 1 + 2 \times 9 + 1 \times 5 = 74$ points; *B* has $4 \times 1 + 3 \times 8 + 2 \times 9 + 1 \times 9 = 55$ points; *C* has $4 \times 9 + 3 \times 9 + 2 \times 0 + 1 \times 9 = 72$ points; *D* has $4 \times 5 + 3 \times 9 + 2 \times 9 + 1 \times 4 = 69$ points.

  (b)   No. No candidate has a majority of the first-place votes.

31.   Winner: *C*. Second place: *D*. Third place: *A*. Last place: *B*.

Step 1. Determine the winner using the plurality-with-elimination method.
       Round 1. *A*: 12; *B*: 1; *C*: 9; *D*: 5. Eliminate *B*.
       Round 2. *A*: 13; *C*: 9; *D*: 5. Eliminate *D*.
       Round 3. *A*: 13; *C*: 14. *C* wins.
       Winner: *C*.
Step 2. Remove the winner (*C*) from the preference schedule and using the plurality-with-elimination method determine the winner from this new preference schedule—this will be the candidate in second place.

Number of voters	12	1	9	5
1st choice	*A*	*B*	*D*	*D*
2nd choice	*B*	*A*	*A*	*B*
3rd choice	*D*	*D*	*B*	*A*

       Round 1. *A*: 12; *B*: 1; *D*: 14. *D* has a majority and wins.
       Second place: *D*.
Step 3. Remove the second place winner (*D*) from the preceding preference schedule and using the plurality-with-elimination method determine the winner from this new preference schedule—this will be the candidate in third place.

Number of voters	21	6
1st choice	*A*	*B*
2nd choice	*B*	*A*

       Round 1. *A*: 21; *B*: 6. *A* has a majority and wins.
       Third place: *A*.
Step 4. This leaves *B* in last place.

33.   Winner: *C*. Second place: *B*. Third place: *D*. Last place: *A*.

Step 1. Determine the winner using the pairwise comparison method. This was done in the text.
       Winner: *C*.
Step 2. Remove the winner (*C*) from the preference schedule and using the pairwise comparison method determine the winner from this new preference schedule—this will be the candidate in second place.

Number of voters	14	14	9
1st choice	*A*	*B*	*D*
2nd choice	*B*	*D*	*B*
3rd choice	*D*	*A*	*A*

       A versus *B* (14 to 23): *B* wins; *A* versus *D* (14 to 23): *D* wins; *B* versus *D* (28 to 9): *B* wins. 0 points for *A*; 2 points for *B*; 1 point for *D*. *B* wins.
       Second place: *B*.
Step 3. Remove the second place winner (*B*) from the preceding preference schedule and using the pairwise comparison method determine the winner from this new preference schedule—this will be the candidate in third place.

Number of voters	14	23
1st choice	A	D
2nd choice	D	A

A versus *D* (14 to 23): *D* wins.
Third place: *D*.
Step 4. This leaves *A* in last place.

35.   Winner: *E*. Second place: *A*. Third place: *B*. Fourth place: *D*. Last place: *C*.

Step 1. Determine the winner using the plurality-with-elimination method.
Round 1. *A*: 8; *B*: 6; *C*: 2; *D*: 3; *E*: 5. Eliminate *C*.
Round 2. *A*: 10; *B*: 6; *D*: 3; *E*: 5. Eliminate *D*.
Round 3. *A*: 10; *B*: 6; *E*: 8. Eliminate *B*.
Round 4. *A*: 10; *E*: 14. *E* wins.
Winner: *E*.

Step 2. Remove the winner (*E*) from the preference schedule and using the plurality-with-elimination method determine the winner from this new preference schedule—this will be the candidate in second place.

Number of voters	8	6	2	3	5
1st choice	A	B	C	D	A
2nd choice	B	D	A	A	D
3rd choice	C	C	B	C	B
4th choice	D	A	D	B	C

Round 1. *A*: 13; *B*: 6; *C*: 2; *D*: 3. *A* has a majority and wins.
Second place: *A*.

Step 3. Remove the second place winner (*A*) from the preceding preference schedule and using the plurality-with-elimination method determine the winner from this new preference schedule—this will be the candidate in third place.

Number of voters	8	6	2	3	5
1st choice	B	B	C	D	D
2nd choice	C	D	B	C	B
3rd choice	D	C	D	B	C

Round 1. *B*: 14; *C*: 2; *D*: 8. *B* has a majority and wins.
Third place: *B*.

Step 4. Remove the third place winner (*B*) from the preceding preference schedule and using the plurality-with-elimination method determine the winner from this new preference schedule—this will be the candidate in fourth place.

Number of voters	10	14
1st choice	C	D
2nd choice	D	C

Round 1. *C*: 10; *D*: 14. *D* has a majority and wins.
Fourth place: *D*.
Step 5. This leaves *C* in last place.

37. Winner: A. Second place: B. Third place: D. Fourth place: E. Last place: C.

Step 1. Determine the winner using the Borda count method.
A has $5 \times 8 + 4 \times 7 + 3 \times 3 + 2 \times 0 + 1 \times 6 = 83$ points; B has $5 \times 6 + 4 \times 8 + 3 \times 0 + 2 \times 7 + 1 \times 3 = 79$ points; C has $5 \times 2 + 4 \times 0 + 3 \times 8 + 2 \times 9 + 1 \times 5 = 57$ points; D has $5 \times 3 + 4 \times 6 + 3 \times 5 + 2 \times 8 + 1 \times 2 = 72$ points; E has $5 \times 5 + 4 \times 3 + 3 \times 8 + 2 \times 0 + 1 \times 8 = 69$ points.
Winner: A.

Step 2. Remove the winner (A) from the preference schedule and using the Borda count method determine the winner from this new preference schedule—this will be the candidate in second place.

Number of voters	8	6	2	3	5
1st choice	B	B	C	D	E
2nd choice	C	D	E	E	D
3rd choice	D	E	B	C	B
4th choice	E	C	D	B	C

B has $4 \times 14 + 3 \times 0 + 2 \times 7 + 1 \times 3 = 73$ points; C has $4 \times 2 + 3 \times 8 + 2 \times 3 + 1 \times 11 = 49$ points; D has $4 \times 3 + 3 \times 11 + 2 \times 8 + 1 \times 2 = 63$ points; E has $4 \times 5 + 3 \times 5 + 2 \times 6 + 1 \times 8 = 55$ points. B wins.
Second place: B.

Step 3. Remove the second place winner (B) from the preceding preference schedule and using the Borda count method determine the winner from this new preference schedule—this will be the candidate in third place.

Number of voters	8	9	2	5
1st choice	C	D	C	E
2nd choice	D	E	E	D
3rd choice	E	C	D	C

C has $3 \times 10 + 2 \times 0 + 1 \times 14 = 44$ points; D has $3 \times 9 + 2 \times 13 + 1 \times 2 = 55$ points; E has $3 \times 5 + 2 \times 11 + 1 \times 8 = 45$ points. D wins.
Third place: D.

Step 4. Remove the third place winner (D) from the preceding preference schedule and using the Borda count method determine the winner from this new preference schedule—this will be the candidate in fourth place.

Number of voters	10	14
1st choice	C	E
2nd choice	E	C

C has $2 \times 10 + 1 \times 14 = 34$ points; E has $2 \times 14 + 1 \times 10 = 38$ points. E wins.
Fourth place: E.

Step 5. This leaves C in last place.

39. Winner: E. Second place: A. Third place: C. Fourth place: B. Last place: D.

Step 1. Determine the winner using the plurality-with-elimination method.
Round 1. A: 5; B: 0; C: 8; D: 3; E: 7. Eliminate B.
Round 2. A: 5; C: 8; D: 3; E: 7. Eliminate D.
Round 3. A: 5; C: 11; E: 7. Eliminate A.
Round 4. C: 11; E: 12. E wins.
Winner: E.

Step 2. Remove the winner (E) from the preference schedule and using the plurality-with-elimination method determine the winner from this new preference schedule—this will be the candidate in second place.

Number of voters	8	3	1	5	6
1st choice	C	D	A	A	A
2nd choice	B	C	B	B	C
3rd choice	D	B	C	D	D
4th choice	A	A	D	C	B

Round 1. A: 12; B: 0; C: 8; D: 3. A wins with a majority of the first-place votes.
Second place: A.

Step 3. Remove the second place winner (A) from the preceding preference schedule and using the plurality-with-elimination method determine the winner from this new preference schedule—this will be the candidate in third place.

Number of voters	8	3	1	5	6
1st choice	C	D	B	B	C
2nd choice	B	C	C	D	D
3rd choice	D	B	D	C	B

Round 1. B: 6; C: 14; D: 3. C wins with a majority of the first-place votes.
Third place: C.

Step 4. Remove the third place winner (C) from the preceding preference schedule and using the plurality-with-elimination method determine the winner from this new preference schedule—this will be the candidate in fourth place.

Number of voters	14	9
1st choice	B	D
2nd choice	D	B

Round 1. B: 14; D: 9. B wins.
Fourth place: B.

Step 5. This leaves D in last place.

Jogging

41. **(a)** 1225

$49 + 48 + 47 + 46 + \ldots + 2 + 1 = (49 \times 50)/2 = 1225$

(b) 2450

Each of the 50 people kisses 49 people, so there are $50 \times 49 = 2450$ kisses.

43. **(a)** Since there are only *two* columns in the preference schedule, one of the columns must represent the votes of 11 or more voters and so the first choice in that column is the first choice of more than half of the voters.

(b) The argument given in (a) can be repeated provided there are an odd number of voters since then one of the *two* columns must represent the votes of more than half of the voters (there cannot be a tie).

45. Suppose that the results of the election under the Borda count method (first place: 5 points, second place: 4 points, third place: 3 points, fourth place: 2 points, and fifth place: 1 point) were

Candidate	A	B	C	D	E
Points	a	b	c	d	e

Under the revised scheme (first place: 4 points, second place: 3 points, third place:

2 points, fourth place: 1 point, and fifth place: 0 points), A loses a point for every voter, so does B, etc. It follows that the result of the election under the revised scheme must be

Candidate	A	B	C	D	E
Points	$a - 21$	$b - 21$	$c - 21$	$d - 21$	$e - 21$

Since these numbers have the same values relative to each other as the original numbers, the outcome of the election is still the same.

47. If there is a candidate that is the first choice of a majority of the voters, then using the plurality-with-elimination method, that candidate will be declared the winner of the election in the first round.

49. If there is a candidate that is the first choice of a majority of the voters, then that candidate will win every head-to-head comparison with any other candidate and so will be a Condorcet candidate. If a voting method violates the majority criterion, then there is an election for which a candidate is the first choice of a majority of the voters (and hence a Condorcet candidate), and yet is not the winner of the election. Consequently, the voting method also violates the Condorcet criterion.

51. **(a)** No. With 27 voters, 14 votes is necessary for a majority.
(b) Yes. C is a Condorcet candidate.

C versus A (15 to 12): C wins; C versus B (19 to 8): C wins; C versus D (15 to 12): C wins.

(c) B

Round 1. A: 10; B: 6; C: 5; D: 6. Eliminate C.
Round 2. A: 10; B: 11; D: 6. Eliminate D.
Round 3. A: 12; B: 15. B wins.

(d) C

Number of voters	10	6	9	2
1st choice	A	B	C	A
2nd choice	C	C	B	B
3rd choice	B	A	A	C

Round 1. A: 12; B: 6; C: 9. Eliminate B.
Round 2. A: 12; C: 15. C wins.

(e) Condorcet criterion. C is a Condorcet candidate but B wins the election using the plurality-with-elimination method.
Independence of irrelevant alternatives criterion. B wins the election using the plurality-with-elimination method, but when D drops out, C wins the election using the plurality-with-elimination method.

53. **(a)** $1523 + 1494 + 1447 = 62 \times (25 + 24 + 23)$ or alternatively, $36 + 25 + 1 = 62$, so all of the first-place votes are accounted for.

(b)

	2nd-place votes	3rd-place votes
Florida State	25	1
Notre Dame	18	19
Nebraska	19	42

Florida State: Let x = the number of 2nd-place votes. Then $1523 = 25 \times 36 + 24 \times x + 23 \times (62 - 36 - x)$ and so $x = 25$. This leaves $62 - 36 - 25 = 1$ 3rd-place vote.
Notre Dame: Let y = the number of 2nd-place votes. Then $1494 = 25 \times 25 + 24 \times y + 23 \times (62 - 25 - y)$ and so $y = 18$. This leaves

62 − 25 − 18 = 19 3rd-place votes.

Nebraska: Let z = the number of 2nd-place votes. Then

$1447 = 25 \times 1 + 24 \times z + 23 \times (62 - 1 - z)$ and so $z = 19$. This leaves

62 − 1 − 19 = 42 3rd-place votes.

Chapter 2: Weighted Voting Systems

Walking

1. **(a)** 4   **(b)** 10   **(c)** 10

    (d) $\{\underline{P_1},\underline{P_2}\},\{\underline{P_1},\underline{P_3}\},\{\underline{P_1},P_2,P_3\},\{\underline{P_1},\underline{P_2},P_4\},\{\underline{P_1},\underline{P_3},P_4\},\{\underline{P_2},\underline{P_3},\underline{P_4}\},\{P_1,P_2,P_3,P_4\}$

    (e) P_1 only

    (f) $P_1 : \frac{5}{12}; P_2 : \frac{1}{4}; P_3 : \frac{1}{4}; P_4 : \frac{1}{12}$.

3. **(a)** $P_1 : \frac{3}{5}; P_2 : \frac{1}{5}; P_3 : \frac{1}{5}$.

    Winning coalitions: $\{\underline{P_1},\underline{P_2}\},\{\underline{P_1},\underline{P_3}\},\{\underline{P_1},P_2,P_3\}$.

    (b) $P_1 : \frac{3}{5}; P_2 : \frac{1}{5}; P_3 : \frac{1}{5}$.

    Winning coalitions: $\{\underline{P_1},\underline{P_2}\},\{\underline{P_1},\underline{P_3}\},\{\underline{P_1},P_2,P_3\}$.
    These are equivalent weighted voting systems.

5. **(a)** $P_1 : \frac{1}{3}; P_2 : \frac{1}{4}; P_3 : \frac{1}{6}; P_4 : \frac{1}{6}; P_5 : \frac{1}{12}$.

    Winning coalitions: $\{\underline{P_1},\underline{P_2},\underline{P_3}\},\{\underline{P_1},\underline{P_2},\underline{P_4}\},\{\underline{P_1},\underline{P_2},\underline{P_5}\},\{\underline{P_1},\underline{P_3},\underline{P_4}\},\{\underline{P_1},P_2,P_3,P_4\},$
    $\{\underline{P_1},\underline{P_2},P_3,P_5\},\{\underline{P_1},\underline{P_2},P_4,P_5\},\{\underline{P_1},\underline{P_3},\underline{P_4},P_5\},\{\underline{P_2},\underline{P_3},\underline{P_4},P_5\},\{P_1,P_2,P_3,P_4,P_5\}$.

    (b) $P_1 : \frac{7}{19}; P_2 : \frac{5}{19}; P_3 : \frac{3}{19}; P_4 : \frac{3}{19}; P_5 : \frac{1}{19}$.

    Winning coalitions: $\{\underline{P_1},\underline{P_2},\underline{P_3}\},\{\underline{P_1},\underline{P_2},\underline{P_4}\},\{\underline{P_1},\underline{P_2},P_3,P_4\},\{\underline{P_1},\underline{P_2},\underline{P_3},P_5\},$
    $\{\underline{P_1},\underline{P_2},\underline{P_4},P_5\},\{\underline{P_1},\underline{P_3},\underline{P_4},P_5\},\{\underline{P_1},P_2,P_3,P_4,P_5\}$.

7. **(a)** $\langle P_1,P_2,P_3\rangle,\langle P_1,P_3,P_2\rangle,\langle P_2,P_1,P_3\rangle,\langle P_2,P_3,P_1\rangle,\langle P_3,P_1,P_2\rangle,\langle P_3,P_2,P_1\rangle$

    (b) $\langle P_1,\underline{P_2},P_3\rangle,\langle P_1,\underline{P_3},P_2\rangle,\langle P_2,\underline{P_1},P_3\rangle,\langle P_2,P_3,\underline{P_1}\rangle,\langle P_3,\underline{P_1},P_2\rangle,\langle P_3,P_2,\underline{P_1}\rangle$

    (c) $P_1 : \frac{2}{3}; P_2 : \frac{1}{6}; P_3 : \frac{1}{6}$.

9. **(a)** $P_1 : 1; P_2 : 0; P_3 : 0$.

    $\langle \underline{P_1},P_2,P_3\rangle,\langle \underline{P_1},P_3,P_2\rangle,\langle P_2,\underline{P_1},P_3\rangle,\langle P_2,P_3,\underline{P_1}\rangle,\langle P_3,\underline{P_1},P_2\rangle,\langle P_3,P_2,\underline{P_1}\rangle$

    (b) $P_1 : \frac{2}{3}; P_2 : \frac{1}{6}; P_3 : \frac{1}{6}$.

    $\langle P_1,\underline{P_2},P_3\rangle,\langle P_1,\underline{P_3},P_2\rangle,\langle P_2,\underline{P_1},P_3\rangle,\langle P_2,P_3,\underline{P_1}\rangle,\langle P_3,\underline{P_1},P_2\rangle,\langle P_3,P_2,\underline{P_1}\rangle$

    (c) $P_1 : \frac{2}{3}; P_2 : \frac{1}{6}; P_3 : \frac{1}{6}$.

    $\langle P_1,\underline{P_2},P_3\rangle,\langle P_1,\underline{P_3},P_2\rangle,\langle P_2,\underline{P_1},P_3\rangle,\langle P_2,P_3,\underline{P_1}\rangle,\langle P_3,\underline{P_1},P_2\rangle,\langle P_3,P_2,\underline{P_1}\rangle$

    (d) $P_1 : \frac{1}{2}; P_2 : \frac{1}{2}; P_3 : 0$.

    $\langle P_1,\underline{P_2},P_3\rangle,\langle P_1,P_3,\underline{P_2}\rangle,\langle P_2,\underline{P_1},P_3\rangle,\langle P_2,P_3,\underline{P_1}\rangle,\langle P_3,P_1,\underline{P_2}\rangle,\langle P_3,P_2,\underline{P_1}\rangle$

    (e) $P_1 : \frac{1}{3}; P_2 : \frac{1}{3}; P_3 : \frac{1}{3}$.

    $\langle P_1,\underline{P_2},P_3\rangle,\langle P_1,\underline{P_3},P_2\rangle,\langle P_2,\underline{P_1},P_3\rangle,\langle P_2,\underline{P_3},P_1\rangle,\langle P_3,\underline{P_1},P_2\rangle,\langle P_3,\underline{P_2},P_1\rangle$

11. **(a)** $P_1 : \frac{1}{2}; P_2 : \frac{3}{10}; P_3 : \frac{1}{10}; P_4 : \frac{1}{10}$.

Winning coalitions: $\left\{\underline{P_1}, \underline{P_2}\right\}, \left\{\underline{P_1}, \underline{P_2}, P_3\right\}, \left\{\underline{P_1}, \underline{P_2}, P_4\right\}, \left\{\underline{P_1}, \underline{P_3}, \underline{P_4}\right\}, \left\{\underline{P_1}, P_2, P_3, P_4\right\}$.

(b) $P_1 : \frac{7}{12}; P_2 : \frac{1}{4}; P_3 : \frac{1}{12}; P_4 : \frac{1}{12}$.

$\left\langle P_1, \underline{P_2}, P_3, P_4\right\rangle, \left\langle P_1, \underline{P_2}, P_4, P_3\right\rangle, \left\langle P_1, P_3, \underline{P_2}, P_4\right\rangle, \left\langle P_1, P_3, \underline{P_4}, P_2\right\rangle, \left\langle P_1, P_4, \underline{P_2}, P_3\right\rangle,$

$\left\langle P_1, P_4, \underline{P_3}, P_2\right\rangle, \left\langle P_2, \underline{P_1}, P_3, P_4\right\rangle, \left\langle P_2, \underline{P_1}, P_4, P_3\right\rangle, \left\langle P_2, P_3, \underline{P_1}, P_4\right\rangle, \left\langle P_2, P_3, P_4, \underline{P_1}\right\rangle,$

$\left\langle P_2, P_4, \underline{P_1}, P_3\right\rangle, \left\langle P_2, P_4, P_3, \underline{P_1}\right\rangle, \left\langle P_3, P_1, \underline{P_2}, P_4\right\rangle, \left\langle P_3, P_1, \underline{P_4}, P_2\right\rangle, \left\langle P_3, P_2, \underline{P_1}, P_4\right\rangle,$

$\left\langle P_3, P_2, P_4, \underline{P_1}\right\rangle, \left\langle P_3, P_4, \underline{P_1}, P_2\right\rangle, \left\langle P_3, P_4, P_2, \underline{P_1}\right\rangle, \left\langle P_4, P_1, \underline{P_2}, P_3\right\rangle, \left\langle P_4, P_1, \underline{P_3}, P_2\right\rangle,$

$\left\langle P_4, P_2, \underline{P_1}, P_3\right\rangle, \left\langle P_4, P_2, P_3, \underline{P_1}\right\rangle, \left\langle P_4, P_3, \underline{P_1}, P_2\right\rangle, \left\langle P_4, P_3, P_2, \underline{P_1}\right\rangle$

13. **(a)** P_1 and P_2 have veto power; P_3 is a dummy.
    (b) P_1 is a dictator; P_2 and P_3 are dummies.
    (c)   There is no dictator, no one has veto power, and no one is a dummy.

15. **(a)** P_1 and P_2 have veto power; P_5 is a dummy.
    (b) P_1 is a dictator; P_2, P_3, P_4 are dummies.
    (c) P_1 and P_2 have veto power; P_3 and P_4 are dummies.
    (d)   All 4 players have veto power.

17. **(a)**   14   **(b)**   27

$$\frac{10+6+5+4+2}{2} < q \le 10+6+5+4+2, \text{ i.e., } 13.5 < q \le 27.$$

    (c)   31   **(d)**   120

$$2^5 - 1 = 31; \ 5! = 1 \times 2 \times 3 \times 4 \times 5 = 120$$

19. **(a)** $P_1 : 1; P_2 : 0; P_3 : 0$.

$\left\langle \underline{P_1}, P_2, P_3\right\rangle, \left\langle \underline{P_1}, P_3, P_2\right\rangle, \left\langle P_2, \underline{P_1}, P_3\right\rangle, \left\langle P_2, P_3, \underline{P_1}\right\rangle, \left\langle P_3, \underline{P_1}, P_2\right\rangle, \left\langle P_3, P_2, \underline{P_1}\right\rangle$

    (b) $P_1 : \frac{2}{3}; P_2 : \frac{1}{6}; P_3 : \frac{1}{6}$.

$\left\langle P_1, \underline{P_2}, P_3\right\rangle, \left\langle P_1, \underline{P_3}, P_2\right\rangle, \left\langle P_2, \underline{P_1}, P_3\right\rangle, \left\langle P_2, P_3, \underline{P_1}\right\rangle, \left\langle P_3, \underline{P_1}, P_2\right\rangle, \left\langle P_3, P_2, \underline{P_1}\right\rangle$

    (c) $P_1 : \frac{1}{2}; P_2 : \frac{1}{2}; P_3 : 0$.

$\left\langle P_1, \underline{P_2}, P_3\right\rangle, \left\langle P_1, P_3, \underline{P_2}\right\rangle, \left\langle P_2, \underline{P_1}, P_3\right\rangle, \left\langle P_2, P_3, \underline{P_1}\right\rangle, \left\langle P_3, P_1, \underline{P_2}\right\rangle, \left\langle P_3, P_2, \underline{P_1}\right\rangle$

    (d) $P_1 : \frac{1}{2}; P_2 : \frac{1}{2}; P_3 : 0$.

$\left\langle P_1, \underline{P_2}, P_3\right\rangle, \left\langle P_1, P_3, \underline{P_2}\right\rangle, \left\langle P_2, \underline{P_1}, P_3\right\rangle, \left\langle P_2, P_3, \underline{P_1}\right\rangle, \left\langle P_3, P_1, \underline{P_2}\right\rangle, \left\langle P_3, P_2, \underline{P_1}\right\rangle$

    (e) $P_1 : \frac{1}{3}; P_2 : \frac{1}{3}; P_3 : \frac{1}{3}$.

$\left\langle P_1, P_2, \underline{P_3}\right\rangle, \left\langle P_1, P_3, \underline{P_2}\right\rangle, \left\langle P_2, P_1, \underline{P_3}\right\rangle, \left\langle P_2, P_3, \underline{P_1}\right\rangle, \left\langle P_3, P_1, \underline{P_2}\right\rangle, \left\langle P_3, P_2, \underline{P_1}\right\rangle$

21. **(a)** 720

$$6! = 1 \times 2 \times 3 \times 4 \times 5 \times 6 = 720$$

(b) 3,628,800

$$10! = 6! \times 7 \times 8 \times 9 \times 10 = 720 \times 7 \times 8 \times 9 \times 10 = 3,628,800$$

(c) $11! = 10! \times 11 = 3,628,800 \times 11 = 39,916,800$

(d) $9! = \dfrac{10!}{10} = \dfrac{3,628,800}{10} = 362,880$

(e) $x = \dfrac{12!}{12} = 11! = 39,916,800$

23. $A : \frac{1}{3}; B : \frac{1}{3}; C : \frac{1}{3}; D : 0.$

Winning coalitions: $\{\underline{A},\underline{B}\}, \{\underline{A},\underline{C}\}, \{\underline{B},\underline{C}\}, \{A,B,C\}, \{\underline{A},\underline{B},D\}, \{\underline{A},\underline{C},D\}, \{\underline{B},\underline{C},D\},$ $\{A,B,C,D\}.$

25. $A : \frac{7}{17}; B : \frac{7}{17}; C : \frac{1}{17}; D : \frac{1}{17}; E : \frac{1}{17}.$

Winning coalitions: $\{\underline{A},\underline{B},\underline{C}\}, \{\underline{A},\underline{B},\underline{D}\}, \{\underline{A},\underline{B},\underline{E}\}, \{\underline{A},\underline{B},C,D\}, \{\underline{A},\underline{B},C,E\},$ $\{\underline{A},\underline{B},D,E\}, \{\underline{A},\underline{B},C,D,E\}.$

Jogging

27. $P_1 : \frac{15}{52}; P_2 : \frac{1}{4}; P_3 : \frac{11}{52}; P_4 : \frac{9}{52}; P_5 : \frac{3}{52}; P_6 : \frac{1}{52}.$

Winning coalitions: $\left\{\underline{P_1},\underline{P_2},\underline{P_3}\right\}, \left\{\underline{P_1},\underline{P_2},\underline{P_4}\right\}, \left\{\underline{P_1},\underline{P_2},\underline{P_5}\right\}, \left\{\underline{P_1},\underline{P_3},\underline{P_4}\right\}, \left\{\underline{P_2},\underline{P_3},\underline{P_4}\right\},$ $\left\{P_1,P_2,P_3,P_4\right\}, \left\{\underline{P_1},\underline{P_2},P_3,P_5\right\}, \left\{\underline{P_1},\underline{P_2},\underline{P_3},P_6\right\}, \left\{\underline{P_1},\underline{P_2},P_4,P_5\right\}, \left\{\underline{P_1},\underline{P_2},\underline{P_4},P_6\right\},$ $\left\{\underline{P_1},\underline{P_2},\underline{P_5},P_6\right\}, \left\{\underline{P_1},\underline{P_3},\underline{P_4},P_5\right\}, \left\{\underline{P_1},\underline{P_3},\underline{P_4},P_6\right\}, \left\{\underline{P_1},\underline{P_3},\underline{P_5},\underline{P_6}\right\}, \left\{\underline{P_2},\underline{P_3},\underline{P_4},P_5\right\},$ $\left\{\underline{P_2},\underline{P_3},\underline{P_4},P_6\right\}, \left\{P_1,P_2,P_3,P_4,P_5\right\}, \left\{P_1,P_2,P_3,P_4,P_6\right\}, \left\{\underline{P_1},P_2,P_3,P_5,P_6\right\},$ $\left\{\underline{P_1},\underline{P_2},P_4,P_5,P_6\right\}, \left\{\underline{P_1},\underline{P_3},P_4,P_5,P_6\right\}, \left\{\underline{P_2},\underline{P_3},\underline{P_4},P_5,P_6\right\}, \left\{P_1,P_2,P_3,P_4,P_5,P_6\right\}.$

29. **(a)** 720
(b) The player must be the last (sixth) player in the sequential coalition.
(c) 120
(d) $\frac{120}{720} = \frac{1}{6}$
(e) $\frac{1}{6}$ (Each player is the last player in 120 of the 720 sequential coalitions.)
(f) If the quota equals the sum of all the weights ($q = w_1 + w_2 + \cdots + w_N$) then the only way a player can be pivotal is for the player to be the last player in the sequential coalition. Since every player will be the last player in the same number of sequential coalitions, all players must have the same Shapley-Shubik power index. It follows that each of the N players has Shapley-Shubik power index of $\frac{1}{N}$.

31. **(a)** [7: 6,3,2,1,1]. Shapley-Shubik power distribution:
$P_1 : \frac{3}{5}; P_2 : \frac{1}{10}; P_3 : \frac{1}{10}; P_4 : \frac{1}{10}; P_5 : \frac{1}{10}.$
(b) [9: 6,3,1,1,1]. Shapley-Shubik power distribution:
$P_1 : \frac{11}{20}; P_2 : \frac{6}{20}; P_3 : \frac{1}{20}; P_4 : \frac{1}{20}; P_5 : \frac{1}{20}.$
(c) [10: 6,3,2,1,1]. Shapley-Shubik power distribution:

$P_1 : \frac{1}{2}; P_2 : \frac{1}{4}; P_3 : \frac{1}{12}; P_4 : \frac{1}{12}; P_5 : \frac{1}{12}.$

(d) [13: 6,3,2,1,1]. Shapley-Shubik power distribution:
$P_1 : \frac{1}{5}; P_2 : \frac{1}{5}; P_3 : \frac{1}{5}; P_4 : \frac{1}{5}; P_5 : \frac{1}{5}.$

33. **(a)** $7 \le q \le 13$

$\frac{8+4+1}{2} < q \le 8+4+1$, i.e., $6.5 < q \le 13$

(b) For $q = 7$ or $q = 8$, P_1 is a dictator since $w_1 = 8 \ge q$.

(c) For $q = 9$, only P_1 has veto power since P_1 is the only player that can single-handedly prevent the rest of the players from passing a motion.

(d) For $10 \le q \le 13$, both P_1 and P_2 have veto power since no motion can pass without both of their votes. (In case $q = 13$, all three players have veto power.)

(e) For $q = 7$ or $q = 8$, both P_2 and P_3 are dummies. For $10 \le q \le 12$, P_3 is a dummy since all winning coalitions contain $\{P_1, P_2\}$ which is itself a winning coalition.

35. **(a)** Both have Banzhaf power distribution $P_1 : \frac{2}{5}; P_2 : \frac{1}{5}; P_3 : \frac{1}{5}; P_4 : \frac{1}{5}.$

(b) In the weighted voting system $[q : w_1, w_2, ..., w_N]$, P_k is critical in a coalition means that the sum of the weights of all the players in that coalition (including P_k) is at least q but the sum of the weights of all the players in the coalition except P_k is less than q. Consequently, if the weights of all the players are multiplied by $c > 0$ ($c \le 0$ would make no sense), then the sum of the weights of all the players in the coalition (including P_k) is at least cq but the sum of the weights of all the players in the coalition except P_k is less than cq. Therefore P_k is critical in the same coalition in the weighted voting system $[cq : cw_1, cw_2, ..., cw_N]$. Since the critical players are the same in both weighted voting systems, the Banzhaf power distributions will be the same.

37. **(a)** If a player X has Banzhaf power index 0 then X is not critical in any coalition and so the addition or deletion of X to or from any coalition will never change the coalition from losing to winning or winning to losing. It follows that X can never be pivotal in any sequential coalition and so X must have Shapley-Shubik power index 0.

(b) If a player X has Shapley-Shubik power index 0 then X is not pivotal in any sequential coalition and so X can never be added to a losing coalition and turn it into a winning coalition. It follows that X can never be critical in any coalition and so X has Banzhaf power index 0.

39. You should buy your vote from P_1. The following table explains why.

Buying a vote from	Resulting weighted voting system	Resulting Banzhaf power distribution	Your power
P_1	[6: 3, 2, 2, 2, 2]	$P_1 : \frac{1}{5}; P_2 : \frac{1}{5}; P_3 : \frac{1}{5}; P_4 : \frac{1}{5}; P_5 : \frac{1}{5}$	$\frac{1}{5}$
P_2	[6: 4, 1, 2, 2, 2]	$P_1 : \frac{1}{2}; P_2 : 0; P_3 : \frac{1}{6}; P_4 : \frac{1}{6}; P_5 : \frac{1}{6}$	$\frac{1}{6}$
P_3	[6: 4, 2, 1, 2, 2]	$P_1 : \frac{1}{2}; P_2 : \frac{1}{6}; P_3 : 0; P_4 : \frac{1}{6}; P_5 : \frac{1}{6}$	$\frac{1}{6}$
P_4	[6: 4, 2, 2, 1, 2]	$P_1 : \frac{1}{2}; P_2 : \frac{1}{6}; P_3 : \frac{1}{6}; P_4 : 0; P_5 : \frac{1}{6}$	$\frac{1}{6}$

41.   **(a)**   You should buy your vote from P_2. The following table explains why.

Buying a vote from	Resulting weighted voting system	Resulting Banzhaf power distribution	Your power
P_1	[18: 9, 8, 6, 4, 3]	$P_1 : \frac{4}{13}; P_2 : \frac{3}{13}; P_3 : \frac{3}{13}; P_4 : \frac{2}{13}; P_5 : \frac{1}{13}$	$\frac{1}{13}$
P_2	[18: 10, 7, 6, 4, 3]	$P_1 : \frac{9}{25}; P_2 : \frac{1}{5}; P_3 : \frac{1}{5}; P_4 : \frac{3}{25}; P_5 : \frac{3}{25}$	$\frac{3}{25}$
P_3	[18: 10, 8, 5, 4, 3]	$P_1 : \frac{5}{12}; P_2 : \frac{1}{4}; P_3 : \frac{1}{6}; P_4 : \frac{1}{12}; P_5 : \frac{1}{12}$	$\frac{1}{12}$
P_4	[18: 10, 8, 6, 3, 3]	$P_1 : \frac{5}{12}; P_2 : \frac{1}{4}; P_3 : \frac{1}{6}; P_4 : \frac{1}{12}; P_5 : \frac{1}{12}$	$\frac{1}{12}$

  (b)   You should buy 2 votes from P_2. The following table explains why.

Buying 2 votes from	Resulting weighted voting system	Resulting Banzhaf power distribution	Your power
P_1	[18: 8, 8, 6, 4, 4]	$P_1 : \frac{7}{27}; P_2 : \frac{7}{27}; P_3 : \frac{7}{27}; P_4 : \frac{1}{9}; P_5 : \frac{1}{9}$	$\frac{1}{9}$
P_2	[18: 10, 6, 6, 4, 4]	$P_1 : \frac{5}{13}; P_2 : \frac{2}{13}; P_3 : \frac{2}{13}; P_4 : \frac{2}{13}; P_5 : \frac{2}{13}$	$\frac{2}{13}$
P_3	[18: 10, 8, 4, 4, 4]	$P_1 : \frac{11}{25}; P_2 : \frac{1}{5}; P_3 : \frac{3}{25}; P_4 : \frac{3}{25}; P_5 : \frac{3}{25}$	$\frac{3}{25}$
P_4	[18: 10, 8, 6, 2, 4]	$P_1 : \frac{9}{25}; P_2 : \frac{7}{25}; P_3 : \frac{1}{5}; P_4 : \frac{1}{25}; P_5 : \frac{3}{25}$	$\frac{3}{25}$

  (c)   Buying a single vote from P_2 raises your power from $\frac{1}{25} = 4\%$ to $\frac{3}{25} = 12\%$.

Buying a second vote from P_2 raises your power to $\frac{2}{13} \approx 15.4\%$. The increase in power is less with the second vote, but if you value power over money, it might still be worth it to you to buy that second vote.

Chapter 3: Fair Division

Walking

1. **(a)** $9.00   **(b)** $3.00

     $C = 3S$; $12 = C + S = 3S + S$; $4S = 12$; $S = 3$; $C = 12 - 3 = 9$.

   (c) $1.00

     $\frac{60°}{180°} \times \$3.00 = \$1.00$

   (d) $2.00

     $\frac{40°}{180°} \times \$9.00 = \$2.00$

   (e) $3.00

     $\left(\frac{60°}{180°} \times \$3.00\right) + \left(\frac{40°}{180°} \times \$9.00\right) = \$1.00 + \$2.00 = \$3.00$

3. **(a)** $6.00   **(b)** $4.00   **(c)** $2.00

     $S = 2V$; $C = 3V$; $12 = S + C + V = 2V + 3V + V = 6V$; $V = 2$, $S = 4$, $C = 6$.

   (d)

     piece 1: $\frac{60°}{120°} \times \$2.00 = \$1.00$;

     piece 2: $\left(\frac{30°}{120°} \times \$2.00\right) + \left(\frac{30°}{120°} \times \$4.00\right) = \$.50 + \$1.00 = \$1.50$;

     piece 3: $\frac{60°}{120°} \times \$4.00 = \$2.00$;

     piece 4: $\left(\frac{30°}{120°} \times \$4.00\right) + \left(\frac{30°}{120°} \times \$6.00\right) = \$1.00 + \$1.50 = \$2.50$;

     piece 5: $\frac{60°}{120°} \times \$6.00 = \$3.00$;

     piece 6: $\left(\frac{30°}{120°} \times \$6.00\right) + \left(\frac{30°}{120°} \times \$2.00\right) = \$1.50 + \$.50 = \$2.00$.

5. Ana: s_2, s_3; Ben: s_3; Cara: s_1, s_2, s_3.

7. Abe: s_1, s_4; Betty: s_1, s_2; Cory: s_1, s_2; Dana: s_4.

9. **(a)**   only (iii)   **(b)**   either

11. **(a)**   Three answers possible as shown in the following table:

Chooser 1	Chooser 2	Divider
s_2	s_1	s_3
s_2	s_3	s_1
s_3	s_1	s_2

(b) Two answers possible as shown in the following table:

Chooser 1	Chooser 2	Divider
s_3	s_1	s_2
s_2	s_1	s_3

(c) The only possible fair division is

Chooser 1	Chooser 2	Divider
s_1	s_2	s_3

(d) The divider can pick between s_2 and s_3—let's say the divider picks s_2. Then s_1 and s_3 can be combined again into a cake that may then be divided between Chooser 1 and Chooser 2 using the divider-chooser method.

13. **(a)** The only possible fair divisions of the cake are

Chooser 1	Chooser 2	Chooser 3	Divider
s_2	s_3	s_1	s_4
s_3	s_1	s_2	s_4

(b) See part (a).
(c) Since none of the choosers have chosen s_4, s_4 can only be given to the divider.

15. **(a)** The only possible fair divisions of the cake are

Chooser 1	Chooser 2	Chooser 3	Chooser 4	Divider
s_2	s_4	s_3	s_5	s_1
s_4	s_2	s_3	s_5	s_1

(b) See part (a).
(c) Since none of the choosers chose s_1, s_1 can only be given to the divider.

17. **(a)** A fair division of the cake is

Chooser 1	Chooser 2	Chooser 3	Chooser 4	Chooser 5	Divider
s_5	s_1	s_6	s_2	s_3	s_4

(b) Chooser 5 must get s_3 which forces chooser 4 to get s_2. This leaves only s_5 for chooser 1 which in turn leaves only s_6 for chooser 3. Consequently only s_1 is left for chooser 2 and the divider gets the left over—s_4.

19. **(a)** Chooser 1: $\{s_3, s_4\}$; chooser 2: $\{s_1, s_3, s_4\}$; chooser 3: $\{s_3\}$
(b) A fair division of the land is

Chooser 1	Chooser 2	Chooser 3	Divider
s_4	s_1	s_3	s_2

21. The value of the parts of the cake (as a percentage of the total) as seen by each person is shown in the figure.

(a) One possible fair division is

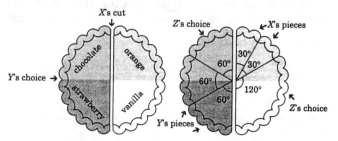

In this division the value of X's final share in X's own eyes is $\frac{2}{3} \cdot 50\% = 33\frac{1}{3}\%$, the value of Y's final share in Y's own eyes is $\frac{2}{3} \cdot 100\% = 66\frac{2}{3}\%$, and the value of Z's final share in Z's own eyes is $\frac{2}{3} \cdot 50\% + 50\% = 83\frac{1}{3}\%$.

(b) One possible fair division is

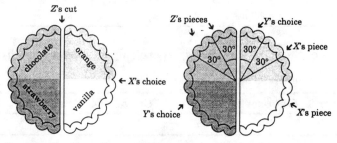

In this division the value of X's final share in X's own eyes is $\frac{2}{3} \cdot 50\% = 33\frac{1}{3}\%$, the value of Y's final share in Y's own eyes is $\frac{1}{3} \cdot 50\% + 50\% + 0\% = 66\frac{2}{3}\%$, and the value of Z's final share in Z's own eyes is $\frac{2}{3} \cdot 50\% = 33\frac{1}{3}\%$.

(c) One possible fair division is

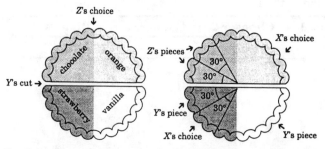

In this division the value of X's final share in X's own eyes is $\frac{1}{3} \cdot 50\% + 50\% = 66\frac{2}{3}\%$, the value of Y's final share in Y's own eyes is $\frac{2}{3} \cdot 50\% = 33\frac{1}{3}\%$, and the value of Z's final share in Z's own eyes is $\frac{2}{3} \cdot 50\% = 33\frac{1}{3}\%$.

23. (a) P_9—P_9 was the last diminisher.
　　(b) P_1—P_1 continues to cut the first piece in each round until he gets a piece.
　　(c) P_{12}
　　(d) P_5—P_5 was the last diminisher.
　　(e) P_1—There were no diminishers.
　　(f) P_2—P_1 got a piece at the end of round 3.
　　(g) P_{12}
　　(h) 11. In the last round, two players get a piece.

25. A gets the desk and receives \$200; B gets the dresser and receives \$80; C gets the vanity and the tapestry and pays \$280.

Item	A	B	C	
Dresser	150.00	300.00 ✔	275.00	
Desk	180.00 ✔	150.00	165.00	
Vanity	170.00	200.00	260.00 ✔	
Tapestry	400.00	250.00	500.00 ✔	
Total Bids	900.00	900.00	1200.00	
Fair Share	300.00	300.00	400.00	Total
Value of items received	180.00	300.00	760.00	Surplus
Prelim. cash settlement	120.00	0.00	−360.00	240.00
Share of surplus	80.00	80.00	80.00	
Final cash settlement	200.00	80.00	−280.00	

27. (a) Bob gets the partnership and pays \$155,000.
　　(b) Jane gets \$80,000 and Ann gets \$75,000.

Item	Bob	Ann	Jane	
Partnership	240000 ✔	210000	225000	
Total Bids	240000	210000	225000	
Fair Share	80000	70000	75000	Total
Value of items received	240000	0	0	Surplus
Prelim. cash settlement	−160000	70000	75000	15000
Share of surplus	5000	5000	5000	
Final cash settlement	−155000	75000	80000	

29. A ends up with items 1, 2, and 4 and must pay \$170,666.66; B ends up with \$90,333.33; C ends up with item 3 and \$80,333.33.

Item	A	B	C	
Item 1	20000 ✔	18000	15000	
Item 2	46000 ✔	42000	35000	
Item 3	3000	2000	4000 ✔	
Item 4	201000 ✔	190000	180000	
Total Bids	270000	252000	234000	
Fair Share	90000	84000	78000	Total
Value of items received	267000	0	4000	Surplus
Prelim. cash settlement	−177000	84000	74000	19000
Share of surplus	6333.34	6333.33	6333.33	
Final cash settlement	−170666.66	90333.33	80333.33	

31. A ends up with items 4 and 5 and pays \$739; B ends up with \$608; C ends up with items 1 and 3 and pays \$261; D ends up with \$632; E ends up with items 2 and 6 and pays \$240.

Item	A	B	C	D	E	
Item 1	352	295	395 ✔	368	324	
Item 2	98	102	98	95	105 ✔	
Item 3	460	449	510 ✔	501	476	
Item 4	852 ✔	852	832	817	843	
Item 5	513 ✔	501	505	505	491	
Item 6	725	738	750	744	761 ✔	
Total Bids	3000	2910	3090	3030	3000	
Fair Share	600	582	618	606	600	Total
Value items rcvd	1365	0	905	0	866	Surplus
Prelim. cash	−765	582	−287	606	−266	130
Share of surplus	26	26	26	26	26	
Final cash	−739	608	−261	632	−240	

33. **(a)** A gets items 10, 11, 12, 13; B gets items 1, 2, 3; C gets items 5, 6, 7.
         (b) Items 4, 8, and 9 are left over.

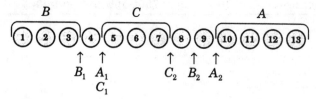

35. **(a)** *A* gets items 1, 2; *B* gets items 10, 11, 12; *C* gets items 4, 5, 6, 7.
(b) Items 3, 8, and 9 are left over.

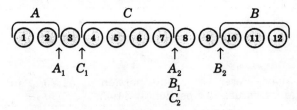

37. **(a)** *A* gets items 19, 20; *B* gets items 15, 16, 17; *C* gets items 1, 2, 3; *D* gets items 11, 12, 13; *E* gets items 5, 6, 7, 8.
(b) Items 4, 9, 10, 14, and 18 are left over.

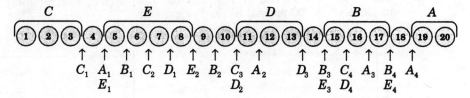

39. **(a)** *A* gets items 4, 5; *B* gets item 10; *C* gets item 15; *D* gets items 1, 2.
(b) Items 3, 6, 7, 8, 9, 11, 12, 13, and 14 are left over.

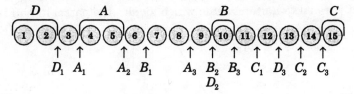

Jogging

41. Paul would choose the larger portion, worth \$2.70 to him.

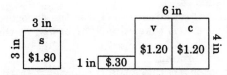

Peter's piece   Paul's choice

Since Paul likes all flavors the same, he would divide his piece into 3 equal (in volume) pieces, each worth \$.90 to him. Peter would also divide his piece into 3 equal (in volume) pieces.

Peter's piece   Paul's choice

Mary would choose any one of Peter's pieces (each worth \$.10 to her) and the vanilla piece from Paul (worth \$1.35 to her).

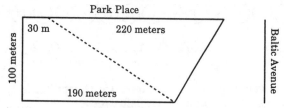

Mary's choice

Mary's eyes

After all is said and done, Peter values his portion at \$1.20, Paul values his portion at \$1.80, and Mary values her portion at \$1.45.

43.   **(a)**   The total area is 30,000 m² and the area of C is only 8000 m². Since P_2 and P_3 value the land uniformly, each thinks that a fair share must have an area of at least 10,000 m².

     (b)   Since there are 22,000 m² left, any cut that divides the remaining property in parts of 11,000 m² will work. For example

Park Place

30 m   220 meters

100 meters

Baltic Avenue

190 meters

     (c)   The cut parallel to Baltic Avenue which divides the parcel in half is

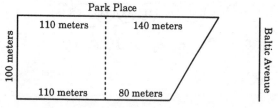

Park Place

110 meters   140 meters

100 meters

Baltic Avenue

110 meters   80 meters

45.   **(a)** H—H was the last diminisher in round 1 and so gets the left breast except for the skin and the part he diminished it.

     (b) G—F was the divider in the last (third) round and so G was the chooser.

     (c) F—F gets what is left after the chooser (G) takes the right breast in the last round.

     (d) F—F was the divider in the last (third) round.

     (e) F—F gets what is left after the chooser (G) takes the right breast in the last round.

     (f) G—H already got a fair share in round 1.

47.   **Step 1 (The Bids).** Each player makes a sealed bid giving his or her honest assessment of the dollar value of each of the items in the estate. **Step 2 (The Allocation).** Each item goes to the highest bidder for that item. (In case of ties, a predetermined tie-breaking procedure should be invoked.) **Step 3 (The Payments).** Each player's fair share is calculated by multiplying the total of that player's bids by the percentage that player is entitled to. (Multiply the total of P_1's bids by $r_1/100$, etc.) Each player puts in or takes out from a common pot (*the estate*) the difference between his or her fair share and the total value of the items allocated to that player. **Step 4 (Dividing the surplus).** After the original allocations are completed there may be a surplus of cash in the estate. This surplus is divided among the players according to the percentage each is entitled to. (P_1 gets $r_1/100$ of the surplus, etc.)

49. Ruth cleans bathrooms and pays \$11.67 per month; Sarah cooks and pays \$11.67 per month; Tamara washes dishes, vacuums, mows the lawn and receives \$23.34 per month.

Item	Ruth	Sarah	Tamara	
Clean bathrooms	−20.00 ✔	−30.00	−40.00	
Do cooking	−50.00	−10.00 ✔	−25.00	
Wash dishes	−30.00	−20.00	−15.00 ✔	
Mow the lawn	−30.00	−20.00	−10.00 ✔	
Vacuum and dust	−20.00	−40.00	−15.00 ✔	
Total Bids	−150.00	−120.00	−105.00	
Fair Share	−50.00	−40.00	−35.00	Total
Value of items received	−20.00	−10.00	−40.00	Surplus
Prelim. cash settlement	−30.00	−30.00	5.00	55.00
Share of surplus	18.33	18.33	18.34	
Final cash settlement	−11.67	−11.67	23.34	

51. The value of the 18 items in each player's eyes is shown in the following tables.

Quintin:

❶	❷	❷	❸	❷	❶	❶	❹	❸	❸	❸	❷	❸	❷	❸	❷	❹	❹	Total
12	7	7	4	7	12	12	6	4	4	4	7	4	7	4	7	6	6	120

Ramon:

❶	❷	❷	❸	❷	❶	❶	❹	❸	❸	❸	❷	❸	❷	❸	❷	❹	❹	Total
9	5	5	5	5	9	9	11	5	5	5	5	5	5	5	5	11	11	120

Stephone:

❶	❷	❷	❸	❷	❶	❶	❹	❸	❸	❸	❷	❸	❷	❸	❷	❹	❹	Total
8	7	7	6	7	8	8	14	6	6	6	7	6	7	6	7	14	14	144

Tim:

❶	❷	❷	❸	❷	❶	❶	❹	❸	❸	❸	❷	❸	❷	❸	❷	❹	❹	Total
5	4	4	4	4	5	5	7	4	4	4	4	4	4	4	4	7	7	84

Consequently, Quintin's fair share (in his value system) is \$30; Ramon's fair share is \$30; Stephone's fair share is \$36; Tim's fair share is \$21.

(a)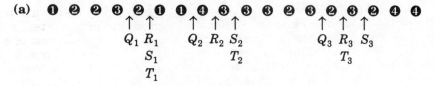

(b)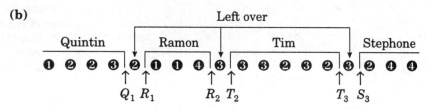

    (c) These are discrete, indivisible items, so the only available methods are the method of markers and the sealed bids method. With only a few items to share, the sealed bid method is appropriate.

53. **(a)** One possible answer is given below.

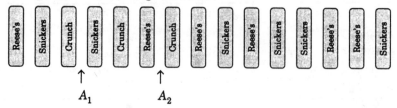

    (b) One possible answer is given below.

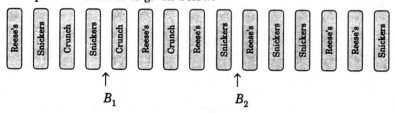

    (c) One possible answer is given below.

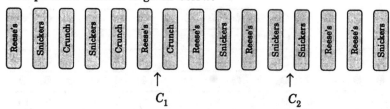

    (d) A gets 1 Nestle Crunch Bar, 1 Reese's Pieces, and 1 Snickers Bar; B gets 1 Snickers Bar, 2 Nestle Crunch Bars, and 2 Reese's Pieces; C gets 2 Snickers Bars and 2 Reese's Pieces.

    (e) 2 Snickers Bars and 1 Reese's Pieces.

55. This problem can be thought of as a fair division problem with 20 players in which 5 of the players are clones of A, 7 of the players are clones of B, and 8 of the players are clones of C.

Chapter 4: The Mathematics of Apportionment

Walking

1. **(a)** 50,000

    SD = (3,310,000 + 2,670,000 + 1,330,000 + 690,000)/160 = 50,000

    (b) A: 66.2; B: 53.4; C: 26.6; D: 13.8

    A: 3,310,000/50,000 = 66.2; B: 2,670,000/50,000 = 53.4;
    C: 1,330,000/50,000 = 26.6; D: 690,000/50,000 = 13.8.

    (c) A: 66; B: 53; C: 27; D: 14

3. **(a)** A: 65.545; B: 52.871; C: 26.337; D: 13.663

    A: 3,310,000/50,500 ≈ 65.545; B: 2,670,000/50,500 ≈ 52.871;
    C: 1,330,000/50,500 ≈ 26.337; D: 690,000/50,500 ≈ 13.663.

    (b) A: 66; B: 53; C: 27; D: 14

5. **(a)** The standard divisor (50,000) works.

    (Any divisor between 49,907 and 50,188 will work.)

    (b) A: 66; B: 53; C: 27; D: 14

7. A: 46; B: 31; C: 21; D: 14; E: 10; F: 8

    (Any divisor between 971 and 975 will work.)

9. A: 45; B: 31; C: 21; D: 14; E: 10; F: 9

    (Any divisor between 995.7 and 999.5 will work.)

11. A: 72; B: 86; C: 51; D: 16

13. A: 72; B: 86; C: 51; D: 16

    (Any divisor between 12.098 and 12.105 will work.)

15. **(a)** 119

    40.50 + 29.70 + 23.65 + 14.60 + 10.55 = 119

    (b) 200,000

    23,800,000/119 = 200,000

    (c) A: 8,100,000; B: 5,940,000; C: 4,730,000; D: 2,920,000; E: 2,110,000

    A: 40.50 × 200,000 = 8,100,000; B: 29.70 × 200,000 = 5,940,000;
    C: 23.65 × 200,000 = 4,730,000; D: 14.60 × 200,000 = 2,920,000;
    E: 10.55 × 200,000 = 2,110,000.

17. A: 41; B: 30; C: 24; D: 14; E: 10

    (Any divisor between 194,667 and 197,083 will work.)

19. A: 40; B: 30; C: 24; D: 15; E: 10

    (Any divisor between 200,953 and 201,276 will work.)

21. Agriculture: 33; Business: 15; Education: 42; Humanities: 21; Science: 139.

23. Agriculture: 33; Business: 15; Education: 42; Humanities: 21; Science: 139.

    (Any divisor between 49.79 and 50.14 will work.)

25. **(a)** Bob: 0; Peter: 3; Ron: 8.

(b) Bob: 1; Peter: 2; Ron: 8.

(c) Yes. For studying an extra 2 minutes (an increase of 3.70%) Bob gets a piece of candy while Peter, who studies an extra 12 minutes (an increase of 4.94%) has to give up a piece. This is an example of the population paradox.

Jogging

27. The same example as given in the previous answer will work. Hamilton's method and Adams' method result in the same apportionment: A: 2; B: 3; C: 2; and D: 3.

29. **(a)** The standard quotas add up to 100. Rounding these standard quotas in the usual way gives A: 11; B: 24; C: 8; D: 36; and E: 20. These integers add up to 99. Consequently, we must choose a divisor that is *smaller* than the standard divisor so that we can obtain modified quotas that are slightly larger.

(b) The standard quotas add up to 100. Rounding these standard quotas in the usual way gives A: 12; B: 25; C: 8; D: 36; and E: 20. These integers add up to 101. Consequently, we must choose a divisor that is *bigger* than the standard divisor so that we can obtain modified quotas that are slightly smaller.

(c) If the standard quotas rounded in the conventional way (to the nearest integer) add up to M, then the standard divisor works as an appropriate divisor for Webster's method.

31. Answers will vary. One such example is: Apportion 90 seats among the four states $A, B, C,$ and D with populations given in the following table. Webster's method results in the apportionment A: 72; B: 7; C: 6; D: 5. Adams' method results in the apportionment A: 69; B: 8; C: 7; D: 6.

State	A	B	C	D
Population	70,800	7400	6400	5400

33. Answers will vary. One such example is: Apportion 90 seats among the four states $A, B, C,$ and D with populations given in the following table. Webster's method apportions 72 seats to state A although state A has a standard quota of 70.8.

State	A	B	C	D
Population	70,800	7400	6400	5400

35. **(a)** A: 5; B: 10; C: 15; D: 21.

(b) For $D = 100$ the modified quotas are A: 5, B: 10, C: 15, D: 20. For $D < 100$, each of the modified quotas above will increase and so rounding upward will give at least A: 6, B: 11, C: 16, D: 21 for a total of at least 54. For $D > 100$, each of the modified quotas above will decrease and so rounding upward will give at most A: 5, B: 10, C: 15, D: 20 for a total of at most 50.

(c) From part (b) we see that there is no divisor such that after rounding the modified quotas upward, the total is 51.

37. (a)

State	Population	Standard quota	Lower quota	Surplus	Final appor.
Connecticut	236,841	6.877	6	1	7
Delaware	55,540	1.613	1	1	2
Georgia	70,835	2.057	2		2
Kentucky	68,705	1.995	1	1	2
Maryland	278,514	8.088	8		8
Massachusetts	475,327	13.803	13	1	14
New Hampshire	141,822	4.118	4		4
New Jersey	179,570	5.214	5		5
New York	331,589	9.629	9	1	10
North Carolina	353,523	10.266	10		10
Pennsylvania	432,879	12.570	12	1	13
Rhode Island	68,446	1.988	1	1	2
South Carolina	206,236	5.989	5	1	6
Vermont	85,533	2.484	2		2
Virginia	630,560	18.310	18		18
Total	3,615,920	105.001	97	8	105

(b)

State	Population	Mod. quota $D = 33000$	Final appor.
Connecticut	236,841	7.177	7
Delaware	55,540	1.683	1
Georgia	70,835	2.147	2
Kentucky	68,705	2.082	2
Maryland	278,514	8.440	8
Massachusetts	475,327	14.404	14
New Hampshire	141,822	4.298	4
New Jersey	179,570	5.442	5
New York	331,589	10.048	10
North Carolina	353,523	10.713	10
Pennsylvania	432,879	13.118	13
Rhode Island	68,446	2.074	2
South Carolina	206,236	6.250	6
Vermont	85,533	2.592	2
Virginia	630,560	19.108	19
Total	3,615,920		105

(c) Virginia; Delaware

39. (a) In Jefferson's method the modified quotas are larger than the standard quotas and so rounding downward will give each state at least the integer part of the standard quota for that state.

(b) In Adams' method the modified quotas are smaller than the standard quota and so rounding upward will give each state at most one more than the integer part of the standard quota for that state.

   (c) If there are only two states, an upper quota violation for one state results in a lower quota violation for the other state (and vice versa). Since neither Jefferson's nor Adams' method can have both upper and lower violations of the quota rule, neither can violate the quota rule when there are only two states.

41. **(a)** Take for example $q_1 = 3.9$ and $q_2 = 10.1$ ($M = 14$). Under both Hamilton's method and Lowndes' method, A gets 4 seats and B gets 10 seats.

      (b) Take for example $q_1 = 3.4$ and $q_2 = 10.6$ ($M = 14$). Under Hamilton's method, A gets 3 seats and B gets 11 seats. Under Lowndes' method, A gets 4 seats and B gets 10 seats.

      (c) If $f_1 > f_2$, then under Hamilton's method the surplus seat goes to A. Under Lowndes' method, the surplus seat would go to B if

$$\frac{f_2}{q_2 - f_2} > \frac{f_1}{q_1 - f_1}.$$

Chapter 5: Euler Circuits

Walking

1. **(a)** Vertices: A, B, C, D; Edges: AB, AC, AD, BD;
    $\deg(A) = 3, \deg(B) = 2, \deg(C) = 1, \deg(D) = 2$.
   (b) Vertices: A, B, C; Edges: none; $\deg(A) = 0, \deg(B) = 0, \deg(C) = 0$.
   (c) Vertices: V, W, X, Y, Z; Edges: $XX, XY, XZ, XV, XW, WY, YZ$;
    $\deg(V) = 1, \deg(W) = 2, \deg(X) = 6, \deg(Y) = 3, \deg(Z) = 2$.

3. **(a)**

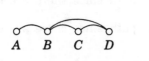 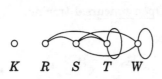

   (b)

5. **(a)** Both graphs have four vertices $A, B, C,$ and D and (the same) edges $AB, AC,$
    AD, BD.
   (b)

7. **(a)**   **(b)**

9. **(a)**   **(b)**

   (c)   **(d)**

11. **(a)** C,B,A,H,F **(b)** C,B,D,A,H,F
    (c) 4 $(C,B,A;\ C,D,A;\ C,B,D,A;\ C,D,B,A)$
    (d) 3 $(H,F;\ H,G,F;\ H,G,G,F)$
    (e) 12 [Any one of the paths in (c) followed by AH, followed by any one of the
     paths in (d)].

13. **(a)** D,C,B,A,D
    (b) 6 $(D,C,B,D;\ D,B,C,D;\ D,A,B,D;\ D,B,A,D;\ D,C,B,A,D;\ D,A,B,C,D)$
     Note: Is the "same" circuit read backward a "different" circuit or not? This is
     always a matter of some controversy but for several reasons it is somewhat
     more convenient to start with the presumption that they are indeed different.

This is consistent with our definition.
(c)   *HA* and *FE*

15.   (a)   None of them.   (b)

17.   (a)   Has an Euler circuit since all vertices have even degree.
(b)   Has no Euler circuit, but has an Euler path since there are exactly two vertices of odd degree.
(c)   Has neither an Euler circuit nor an Euler path since there are four vertices of odd degree.

19.   (a)   Has an Euler circuit since all vertices have even degree.
(b)   Has no Euler circuit, but has an Euler path since there are exactly two vertices of odd degree.
(c)   Has no Euler circuit, but has an Euler path since there are exactly two vertices of odd degree.

21.   (a)   Neither since there are more than two vertices of odd degree.

(b)   Open unicursal tracing.   (c)   Open unicursal tracing.

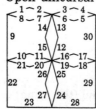   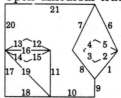

23.   (a)   (b)

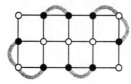   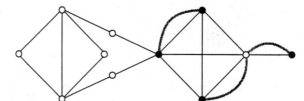

25.   (a)   (b)

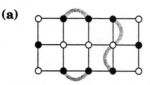   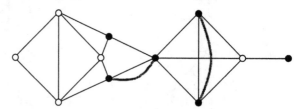

27.

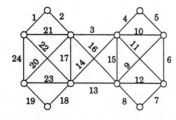

29.   *A,B,C,D,E,F,G,A,C,E,G,B,D,F,A,D,G,C,F,B,E,A*

31.

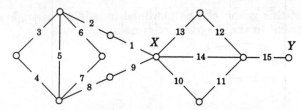

33. **(a)**

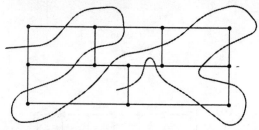

(b) *BC* and *JK*

35. An optimal semi-eulerization of the graph corresponding to the diagram is

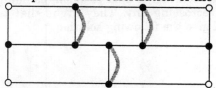

Each added edge requires either a retracing or a lifting of your pencil. Therefore, you would have to lift your pencil 3 times.

37.

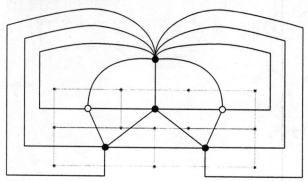

The graph for this problem would have 6 vertices (corresponding to the 5 rectangles and the outside) and 16 edges (corresponding to the line segments that need to be crossed.

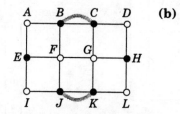

Since a semi-eulerization of this graph can be obtained by adding a single edge, we can cross every line segment in the diagram, re-crossing only one.

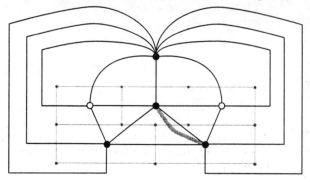

Note: Some "puzzle solvers" give a "trick" solution to this problem, claiming they can cross every line segment without recrossing any. They argue that tracing over a line segment is not crossing it and give the following solution.

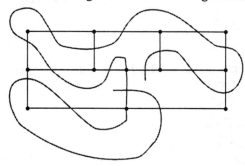

Jogging

39. **(a)**

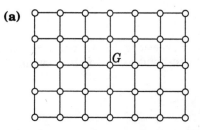

(b)

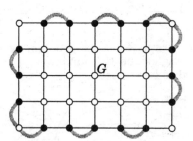

(c)

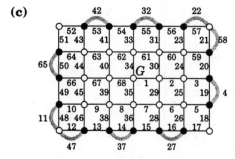

41. (a)

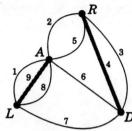

Eulerizing the graph shown in Fig. 5-18(b) requires the addition of two edges so the cheapest walk will cost $9.00. One possible such walk is shown in the figure.

(b)

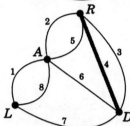

Semi-eulerizing the graph shown in Fig. 5-18(b) requires the addition of one edge so the cheapest walk will cost $8.00. One possible such walk (starting at L and ending at A) is shown in the figure.

43. (a)

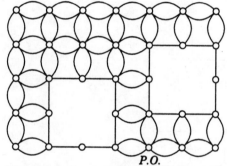

(b) The graph is already eulerized.

(c)

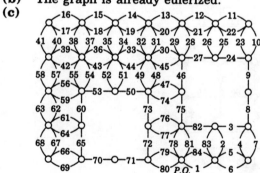

45.

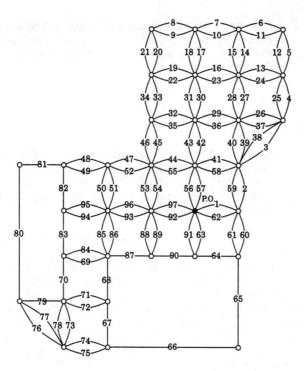

47.   **(a)**   12

       (b)

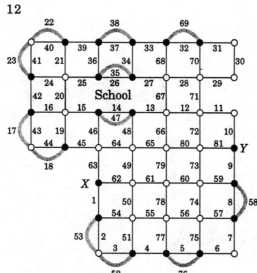

49. **(a)** The office complex can be represented by a graph (where each vertex represents a location and each edge a door).

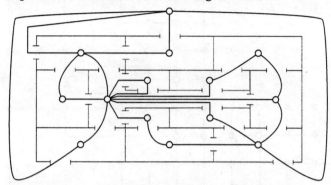

Since there are vertices of odd degree (for example the secretary's office has degree 3) there is no Euler circuit.

(b) Since there are exactly 2 vertices of odd degree (the secretary's office has degree 3 and the hall has degree 9), there is an Euler path starting at either the secretary's office or the hall and ending at the other.

(c) If the door from the secretary's office to the hall is removed (i.e., the edge between the secretary's office and the hall is removed), then every vertex will have even degree and so there will be an Euler circuit. Consequently, it would be possible to start at any location, walk through every door exactly once and end up at the starting location.

51. **(a)**

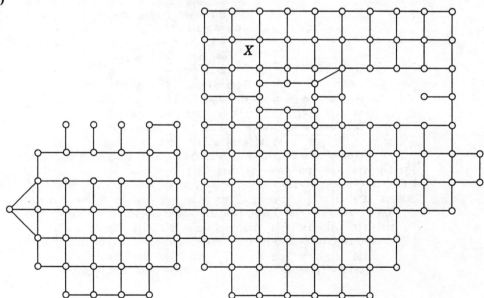

(b)

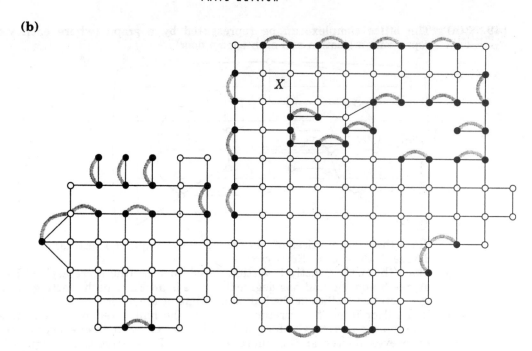

(c)

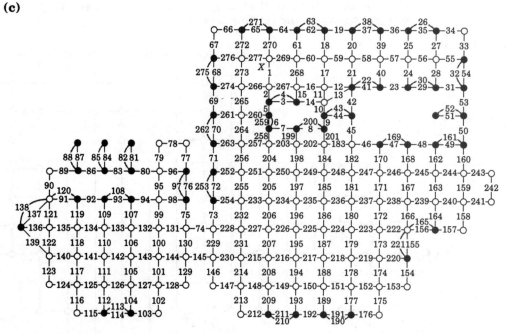

Chapter 6: The Traveling-Salesman Problem

Walking

1. **(a)** *A, D, B, E, C, F, G, A*

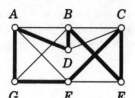

   (b) *A, G, F, E, C, D, B*

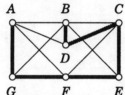

   (c) *D, A, G, B, C, E, F*

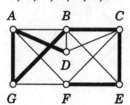

3. First note that edges *CD* and *DE* must be a part of every Hamilton circuit and that *CE* cannot be a part of any Hamilton circuit.

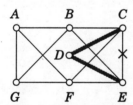

   There are 2 possibilities at vertex *C*: edge *BC* or edge *CF*. Edge *BC* forces edge *FE* (otherwise there would be a circuit *E, B, C, D, E*) and edge *CF* forces edge *EB*.

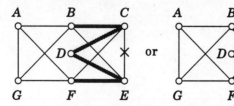

   The first of these can be completed in 2 ways giving Hamilton circuits *A, B, C, D, E, F, G, A* and *A, F, E, D, C, B, G, A* along with their mirror-image circuits *A, G, F, E, D, C, B, A* and *A, G, B, C, D, E, F, A*.

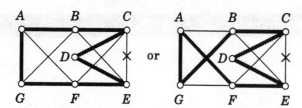

The second of these can also be completed in 2 ways giving Hamilton circuits A, B, E, D, C, F, G, A and A, F, C, D, E, B, G, A along with their mirror-image circuits A, G, F, C, D, E, B, A and A, G, B, E, D, C, F, A.

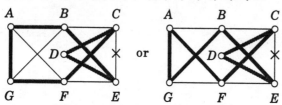

5.   **(a)** A, F, B, C, G, D, E, A A, F, B, E, C, G, D, A

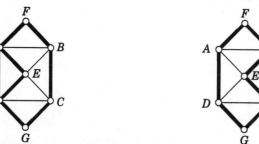

(b) A, F, B, C, G, D, E

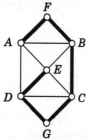

(c) A, F, B, E, D, G, C

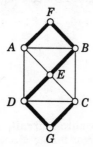

(d) F, A, B, E, D, C, G

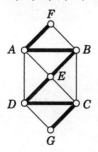

7. Edges AF, AB, ED, and DC must be a part of every Hamilton circuit. Edge EC cannot be a part of any Hamilton circuit.

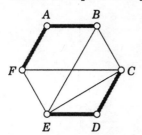

This can be completed to give a Hamilton circuits in 2 ways.

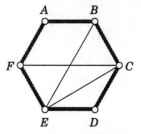   or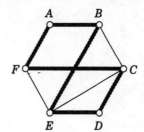

(a) A, B, C, D, E, F, A and A, B, E, D, C, F, A along with their mirror-image circuits A, F, E, D, C, B, A and A, F, C, D, E, B, A.

(b) D, E, F, A, B, C, D and D, C, F, A, B, E, D along with their mirror-image circuits D, C, B, A, F, E, D and D, E, B, A, F, C, D. (These are the same circuits given in (a), just written with a different starting vertex.)

9. The degree of every vertex in a graph with a Hamilton circuit must be at least 2 since the circuit must "pass through" every vertex. A graph with a Hamilton path can have at most 2 vertices (the starting and ending vertices of the path) of degree 1 since the path must "pass through" the remaining vertices. This graph has 4 vertices of degree 1.

11. **(a)** 6   **(b)** 4

     (c) A, B, C, D, E, A with weight $8 + 7 + 3 + 5 + 9 = 32$

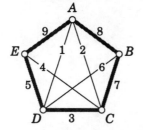

(d)   *A, D, B, C, E, A* with weight $1 + 6 + 7 + 4 + 9 = 27$

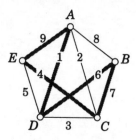

13.   **(a)**   11

     (b)   *A, B, C, F, E, D, A* with weight $10 + 11 + 6 + 5 + 3 + 2 = 37$

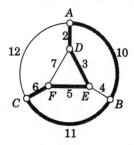

     (c)   *A, D, F, E, B, C, A* with weight $2 + 7 + 5 + 4 + 11 + 12 = 41$

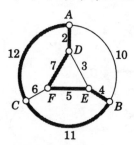

15.   **(a)** $6! = 5! \times 6 = 120 \times 6 = 720$

     (b) $9! = \dfrac{10!}{10} = 362{,}880$

     (c) $9! = 362{,}880$

17.   **(a)**

Hamilton circuit	Weight	Mirror-image circuit
A, B, C, D, A	$38 + 22 + 8 + 12 = 80$	*A, D, C, B, A*
A, B, D, C, A	$38 + 10 + 8 + 18 = 74$	*A, C, D, B, A*
A, C, B, D, A	$18 + 22 + 10 + 12 = 62$	*A, D, B, C, A*

Optimal Hamilton circuit: *A, C, B, D, A* with weight 62.

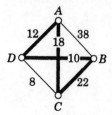

     (b)   *A, D, C, B, A* with weight 80

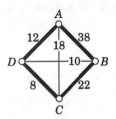

(c) A, B, D, C, A with weight 74

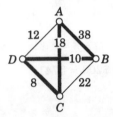

(d)   The solution obtained in part (b) is **29.0% more expensive than the optimal solution found in part (a)**—relative error = $(80 - 62)/62 \approx 0.290$. **The solution obtained in part (c) is 19.4% more expensive than the optimal solution**—relative error = $(74 - 62)/62 \approx 0.194$.

19.   **(a)** B, C, A, E, D, B; $121 + $119 + $133 + $199 + $150 = $722.

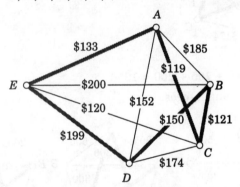

       (b) C, A, E, D, B, C; $119 + $133 + $199 + $150 + $121 = $722.

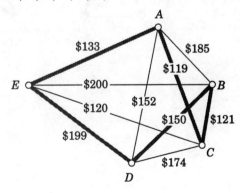

(c) D, B, C, A, E, D; $150 + $121 + $119 + $133 + $199 = $722.

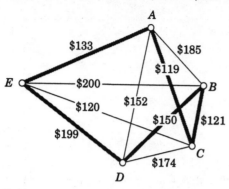

(d) E, C, A, D, B, E; $120 + $119 + $152 + $150 + $200 = $741.

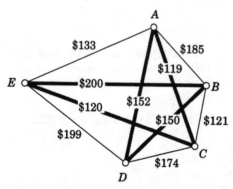

21. A, D, B, E, C, A; $185 + 360 + 340 + 165 + 200 = 1250.$

The steps are shown in the following figures.

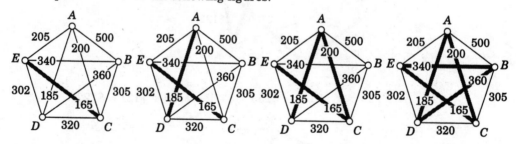

23.

Hamilton circuit	Weight	Mirror-image circuit
A, B, C, D, E, A	$500 + 305 + 320 + 302 + 205 = 1632$	A, E, D, C, B, A
A, B, C, E, D, A	$500 + 305 + 165 + 302 + 185 = 1457$	A, D, E, C, B, A
A, B, D, C, E, A	$500 + 360 + 320 + 165 + 205 = 1550$	A, E, C, D, B, A
A, B, D, E, C, A	$500 + 360 + 302 + 165 + 200 = 1527$	A, C, E, D, B, A
A, B, E, C, D, A	$500 + 340 + 165 + 320 + 185 = 1510$	A, D, C, E, B, A
A, B, E, D, C, A	$500 + 340 + 302 + 320 + 200 = 1662$	A, C, D, E, B, A
A, C, B, D, E, A	$200 + 305 + 360 + 302 + 205 = 1372$	A, E, D, B, C, A
A, C, B, E, D, A	$200 + 305 + 340 + 302 + 185 = 1332$	A, D, E, B, C, A
A, C, D, B, E, A	$200 + 320 + 360 + 340 + 205 = 1425$	A, E, B, D, C, A
A, C, E, B, D, A	$200 + 165 + 340 + 360 + 185 = 1250$	A, D, B, E, C, A
A, D, B, C, E, A	$185 + 360 + 305 + 165 + 205 = 1220$	A, E, C, B, D, A
A, D, C, B, E, A	$185 + 320 + 305 + 340 + 205 = 1355$	A, E, B, C, D, A

Optimal Hamilton circuit: A, D, B, C, E, A with a cost of \$1220.

25. E, P, C, H, T, G, E; $2.3 + 1.8 + 3.2 + 2.1 + 1.9 + 1.2 = 12.5$ years.

The steps are shown in the following figures.

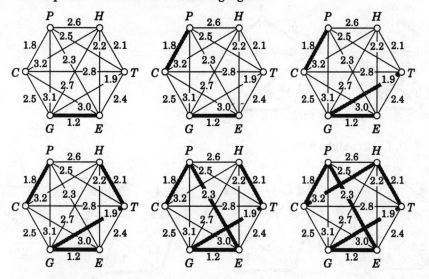

27. **(a)** A, E, B, C, D, A (weight 63)

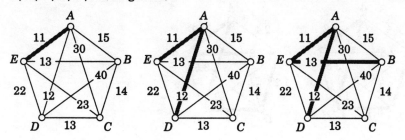

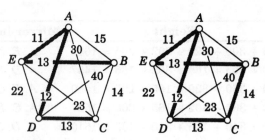

(b)   No. The 5 edges used in the Hamilton circuit are the 5 cheapest edges in the graph.

29.   *A, E, C, D, B, A* (weight 91)

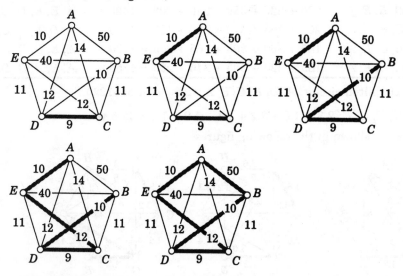

31.   *A, B, E, D, C, A* (weight 9.9)

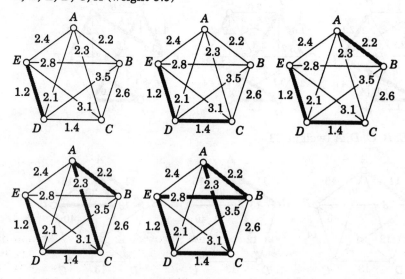

33. *C, D, E, A, B, C* (weight 9.8)

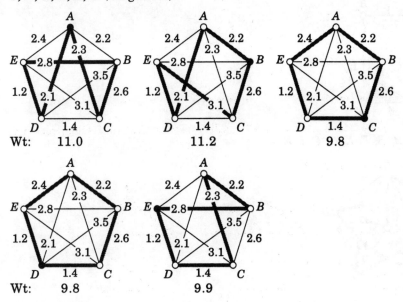

Wt: 11.0   11.2   9.8

Wt: 9.8   9.9

35. *A, B, F, C, D, E, A* (weight 203)

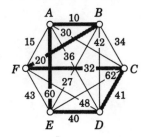

37. **(a)**

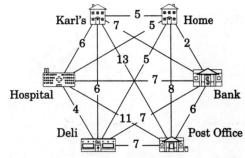

(b) Home, Bank, Post Office, Deli, Hospital, Karl's, Home. The total length of the trip is 30 miles.

Jogging

39. Each vertex is adjacent to each of the other vertices, so each vertex has degree $N - 1$. Since there are N vertices, the sum of the degrees of all the vertices is $N(N - 1)$. But the sum of the degrees of all the vertices in a graph is always equal to twice the number of edges. Therefore, the number of edges in a complete graph with N vertices is $N(N - 1)/2$.

41.

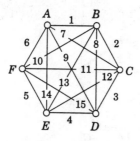

43. $A, J, D, H, B, F, K, G, C, I, E, A$

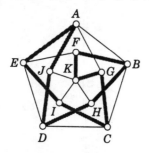

45. $A, B, C, D, J, I, F, G, E, H$

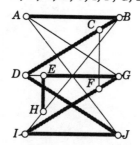

47. **(a)** $2^3 = 8 > 6 = 3!$ **(b)** $2^4 = 16 < 24 = 4!$
(c) $N!$ is bigger.

$$2^5 = 2 \cdot 2^4 < 2 \cdot 4! < 5 \cdot 4! = 5!$$

$$2^6 = 2 \cdot 2^5 < 2 \cdot 5! < 6 \cdot 5! = 6!$$

$$2^7 = 2 \cdot 2^6 < 2 \cdot 6! < 7 \cdot 6! = 7!$$

$$\vdots$$

$$2^{k+1} = 2 \cdot 2^k < 2 \cdot k! < (k+1) \cdot k! = (k+1)!$$

$$\vdots$$

In other words, as k increases by 1, 2^k increases by a factor of 2, but $k!$ increases by a factor of $(k + 1)$.

49. Dallas, Houston, Memphis, Louisville, Columbus, Chicago, Kansas City, Denver, Atlanta, Buffalo, Boston, Dallas.

Chapter 7: The Mathematics of Networks

Walking

1. **(a)** tree   **(b)** not a tree (has a circuit, is not connected)
   (c) not a tree (has a circuit)   **(d)** tree

3.

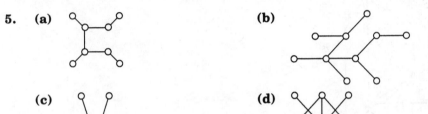

5. **(a)**   **(b)**

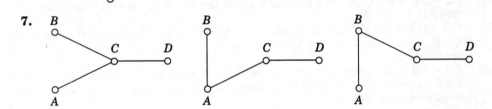

   (c)   **(d)**

7.

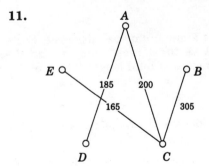

9. **(a)** 3

   Removing one of the 3 edges of the circuit gives a spanning tree.

   (b) 1

   The graph is a tree and hence is its only spanning tree.

11.

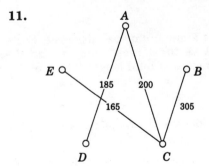

13.

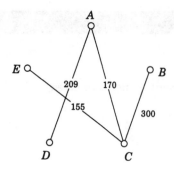

15.

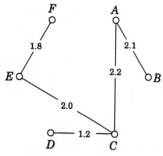

17. **(a)** $CE + ED + EB$ is larger since $CD + DB$ is the shortest network connecting the cities C, D, and B.

    (b) $CD + DB$ is the shortest network connecting the cities C, D, and B since angle CDB is 120° and so the shortest network is the same as the minimum spanning tree.

    (c) $CE + EB$ is the shortest network connecting the cities C, E, and B since angle CEB is more than 120° and so the shortest network is the same as the minimum spanning tree.

19. 88.2

Since the side opposite $\angle C$ is larger than the side opposite $\angle B$, we must have $\angle B < \angle C = 30°$ and so $\angle B + \angle C < 60°$. This makes $\angle A > 120°$ and so the shortest network connecting A, B, and C is the minimum spanning tree of length $40.4 + 47.8 = 88.2$.

21. 50.6

Since $\angle A = 140° > 120°$, the shortest network is a minimum spanning tree. Since $\angle A$ is the largest angle, the side opposite $\angle A$ is the largest side and so the minimum spanning tree consists of the other two sides of total length $20.1 + 30.5 = 50.6$.

23. **(a)** BC

    The longest side of the triangle is the side opposite the largest angle, i.e., the side opposite $\angle A$.

    (b) $AB + AC$

    (c) No. Since all the angles of the triangle are less than 120°, the shortest network is a Steiner tree of length less than that of the minimum spanning tree.

25. $\sqrt{3}AB$

Extend AS to meet side BC at J (see figure). It is easy to see that $\triangle SJB$ is a 30°-60°-90° triangle. In a 30°-60°-90° triangle, the side opposite the 60° angle is $\frac{\sqrt{3}}{2}$ times the hypotenuse. Therefore, $JB = \frac{\sqrt{3}}{2}SB$ and so $BC = JB + JC$ $= 2JB = \sqrt{3}SB$ or $SB = \frac{\sqrt{3}}{3}BC$. Consequently, $SA + SB + SC = 3SB = \sqrt{3}BC = \sqrt{3}AB = \sqrt{3}AC$.

Jogging

27.   The minimum cost network connecting the 4 cities has a 3-way junction point at A and has a total cost of 205 million dollars.

29.   In a tree there is one and only one path joining any two vertices. Consequently, the only path joining two adjacent vertices is the edge connecting them and so if that edge is removed, the graph will become disconnected.

31.   **(a)**   27

To get a spanning tree, one of the edges of the circuit A, B, C, A must be removed along with one of the edges of the circuit D, E, F, D and one of the edges of the circuit G, H, I, G. There are 3 ways to do each of these, for a total of $3 \times 3 \times 3 = 27$ possible spanning trees.

      (b)   18

To get a spanning tree, one of the edges of the circuit A, B, C, A must be removed along with one of the edges of the circuit D, E, F, G, H, I, D. There are 3 ways to do the former and 6 ways to do the latter for a total of $3 \times 6 = 18$ possible spanning trees.

      (c)   42

To get a spanning tree, one of the edges of the circuit A, B, C, D, E, F, A must be removed along with one of the edges of the circuit G, H, I, J, K, L, M, G. There are 6 ways to do the former of these and 7 ways to do the latter, for a total of $6 \times 7 = 42$ possible spanning trees.

33.   **(a)**   According to Cayley's theorem, there are $3^{3-2} = 3$ spanning trees in a complete graph with 3 vertices and $4^{4-2} = 16$ spanning trees in a complete graph with 4 vertices.

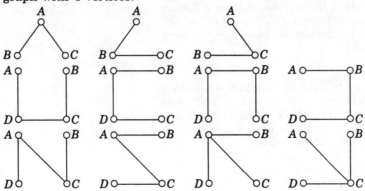

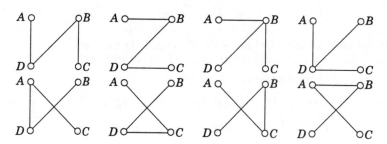

(b) There are $(N-1)!$ Hamilton circuits and N^{N-2} spanning trees in a complete graph with N vertices. Since

$$\frac{(N-1)!}{N^{N-2}} = \frac{2}{N} \times \frac{3}{N} \times \frac{4}{N} \times \cdots \times \frac{N-1}{N} < \frac{2}{N} < 1 \text{ for } N \geq 3,$$

there are more spanning trees than there are Hamilton circuits.

35. **(a)** ○———○———○———○

     (b) ○———○———○———○———○

     (c) ○———○———○ ⋯ ○———○———○

37. **(a)** 2. The solution of Exercise 35(c) shows an example of a graph with N vertices with only 2 vertices of degree 1. To show that there cannot be any fewer vertices of degree 1, let v be the number of vertices in the graph, e the number of edges, and k the number of vertices of degree 1. Recall that in a tree $v = e + 1$ and in any graph the sum of the degrees of all the vertices is $2e$. Now, since we are assuming there are exactly k vertices of degree 1, the remaining $v - k$ vertices must have degree at least 2. Therefore the sum of the degrees of all the vertices must be at least $k + 2(v - k)$. Putting all this together we have

$$2e \geq k + 2(v - k) = k + 2(e + 1 - k),$$
$$2e \geq k + 2e + 2 - 2k,$$
$$k \geq 2.$$

     (b) $N - 1$. The solution of Exercise 36(c) shows an example of a graph with N vertices with $N - 1$ vertices of degree 1. It is clear that there cannot be any more vertices of degree 1, since the graph must be connected and so there must be at least one vertex of degree more than 1 if there are more than 2 vertices.

39. If some edge had weight more than the weight of e, deleting that edge would result in a spanning tree with total weight less than that of the minimum spanning tree.

41. **(a)** If J is a Steiner point then $\angle BJC = 120°$. But since $\angle BJC > \angle BAC = 130°$, this is impossible. [See part (b) for a proof.]

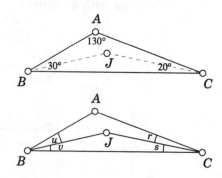

     (b) In $\triangle ABC$, $\angle BAC + \angle ABC + \angle BCA = \angle BAC + u + v + r + s = 180°$ (see figure). In $\triangle BJC$, $\angle BJC + v + s = 180°$. Therefore, $\angle BAC + u + v + r + s = \angle BJC + v + s$ and so $\angle BAC + u + r = \angle BJC$. Consequently, $\angle BAC < \angle BJC$ and so if $\angle BAC > 120°$ then $\angle BJC > 120°$. Thus, J cannot be a Steiner point since $\angle BJC \neq 120°$.

43. The length of the network is $4x$ (see figure). Since the diagonals of a square are perpendicular, by the Pythagorean theorem we have $x^2 + x^2 = 500^2$ which gives $2x^2 = 500^2$ or $x = \dfrac{500}{\sqrt{2}} = \dfrac{500\sqrt{2}}{2} = 250\sqrt{2}$. Thus $4x = 1000\sqrt{2} \approx 1414$.

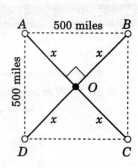

45. **(a)** The length of the network is $4x + (300 - x)$ $= 3x + 300$, where $200^2 + \left(\dfrac{x}{2}\right)^2 = x^2$. (See figure.) Solving the equation gives $x = \dfrac{400\sqrt{3}}{3}$, and so the length of the network is $400\sqrt{3} + 300 \approx 993$.

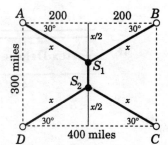

(b) The length of the network is $4x + (400 - x)$ $= 3x + 400$, where $150^2 + \left(\dfrac{x}{2}\right)^2 = x^2$. (See figure.) Solving the equation gives $x = \dfrac{300\sqrt{3}}{3}$, and so the length of the network is $300\sqrt{3} + 400 \approx 919.6$.

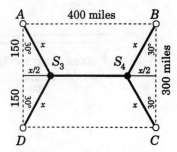

47. Because of Exercise 37(a), if all the vertices had the same degree, they would all have to have degree 1 and the sum of the degrees of all the vertices would be N. This is impossible when $N \geq 3$ since in a tree with N vertices the sum of the degrees of all the vertices is $2N - 2$, and for $N \geq 3$, $2N - 2 > N$.

Chapter 8: The Mathematics of Scheduling

Walking

1. (a)

Vertex	Degree	Indegree	Outdegree	Vertex is incident to	Vertex is incident from
A	3	2	1	C	B, D
B	2	0	2	A, D	–
C	1	1	0	–	A
D	2	1	1	A	B

(b)

Vertex	Degree	Indegree	Outdegree	Vertex is incident to	Vertex is incident from
A	4	2	2	B, C	C, E
B	2	1	1	D	A
C	4	1	3	A, D, E	A
D	3	3	0	–	B, C, E
E	3	1	2	A, D	C

(c)

Vertex	Degree	Indegree	Outdegree	Vertex is incident to	Vertex is incident from
A	1	1	0	–	B
B	3	2	1	A	E
C	2	1	1	F	E
D	1	1	0	–	E
E	5	0	5	B, C, D, F	–
F	2	2	0	–	C, E

3. (a) 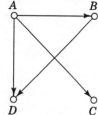 (b)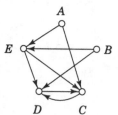

5.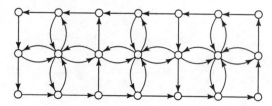

7. (a) 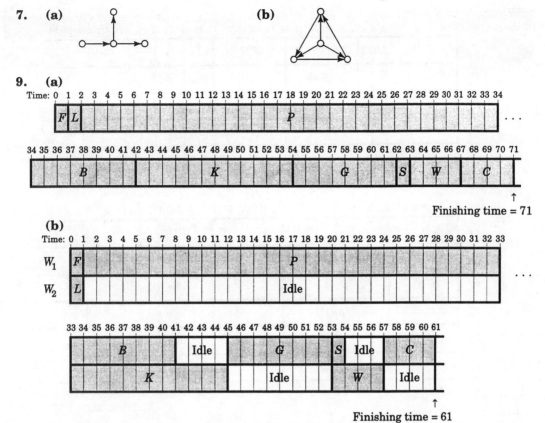   (b)

9. (a)

(b)

Finishing time = 71

Finishing time = 61

11. According to the precedence relations, G cannot be started until K is completed.

13. According to the precedence relations, G cannot be started until both K and B are completed.

15.

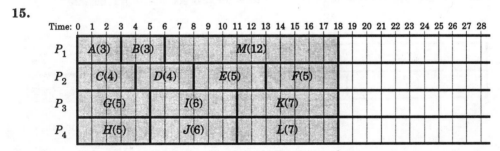

Finishing time = 18

17.

Time: 0 1 2 3 4 5 6 7 8 9 10 11 12 13 14 15 16 17 18 19 20 21 22 23 24 25 26 27 28

Processor	Tasks
P_1	M(12), F(5), Idle
P_2	L(7), H(5), E(5), Idle
P_3	K(7), G(5), D(4), B(3)
P_4	J(6), I(6), C(4), A(3)

Finishing time = 19

19.

Time: 0 1 2 3 4 5 6 7 8 9 10 11 12 13 14 15 16 17 18 19 20 21 22 23 24

Processor	Tasks
P_1	A(3), L(7), M(12)
P_2	B(3), K(7), Idle
P_3	C(4), J(6), Idle
P_4	D(4), I(6), Idle
P_5	E(5), H(5), Idle
P_6	F(5), G(5), Idle

Finishing time = 22

21. No. The total length of the 13 copying jobs is 72 minutes. If 5 processors are going to do 72 minutes of work with no idle time, each processor must do $\frac{72}{5} = 14.4$ minutes of work. Since all of the jobs require a whole number of minutes to complete, a completion time of 14.4 minutes for a processor is impossible.

23.

Time: 0 1 2 3 4 5 6 7 8 9 10 11 12 13 14 15 16 17 18 19 20 21 22 23 24 25 26

Processor	Tasks
P_1	C(9), E(6), G(2), Idle, F
P_2	A(8), B(5), D(12), Idle

Finishing time = 26

25.

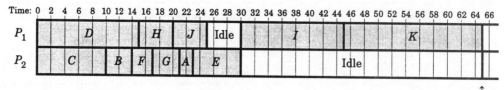

Time: 0 2 4 6 8 10 12 14 16 18 20 22 24 26 28 30 32 34 36 38 40 42 44 46 48 50 52 54 56 58 60 62 64 66

Processor	Tasks
P_1	D, H, J, Idle, I, K
P_2	C, B, F, G, A, E, Idle

Finishing time = 65

27.

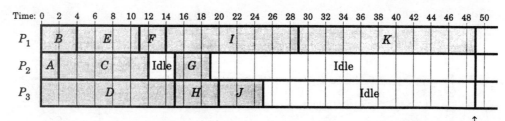

Finishing time = 49

29. Since there is a total of 25 hours of work to be done by 2 processors, the work cannot be completed in less than 12.5 hours. But the times for all the jobs are whole numbers, so the work cannot be completed in less than 13 hours.

31.

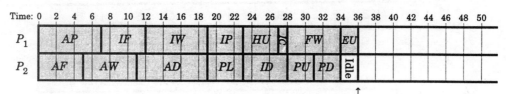

Finishing time = 36

33. **(a)**

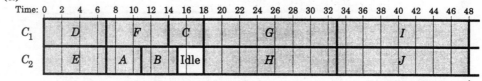

Finishing time = 48

(b)

Time: 0 2 4 6 8 10 12 14 16 18 20 22 24 26 28 30 32 34 36 38 40 42 44 46 48

C_1	D	A	G	J
C_2	E	B	H	Idle
C_3	F	C	I	Idle

Finishing time = 41

(c)

Time: 0 2 4 6 8 10 12 14 16 18 20 22 24 26 28 30 32 34 36 38 40 42 44 46 48

C_1	D	C	G
C_2	E	Idle	H
C_3	F	Idle	I
C_4	A	B	Idle	J

Finishing time = 26

35.

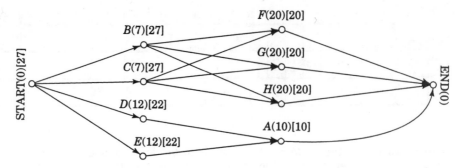

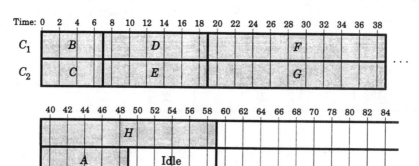

37. (a)

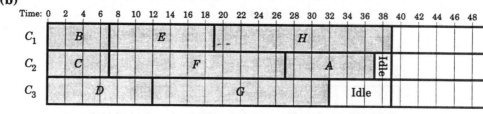

Finishing time = 59

(b)

Finishing time = 39

39. (a)

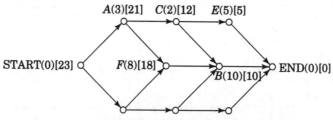

Note: The critical path times shown inside the square brackets are not required for part (a), but are included for part (b).

(b)

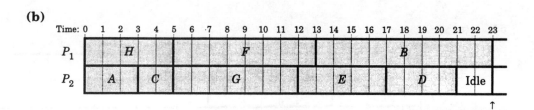

Finishing time = 23

Jogging

41. Each arc of the graph contributes 1 to the sum of the indegrees and 1 to the sum of the outdegrees.

43. **(a)** True. If no processor is idle, then the total of the processing times of all the tasks is the same as the completion time of the schedule and so there can be no shorter schedule.

(b) False. Precedence relations may force idle time for one or more processors.

45. **(a)** $\frac{4}{15}$, $\frac{5}{18}$, $\frac{6}{21}$, $\frac{7}{24}$, $\frac{8}{27}$, $\frac{9}{30}$

(b) Since $M - 1 \le M$, we have $\frac{M-1}{3M} \le \frac{M}{3M} = \frac{1}{3}$.

47. **(a)**

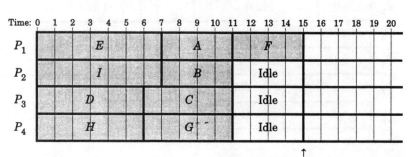

Finishing time = 15

(b)

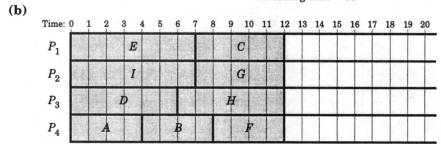

Finishing time = 12

49.

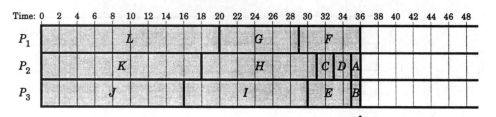

Finishing time = 36

This schedule is obviously optimal, since the processors are always busy.

51.   **(a)**

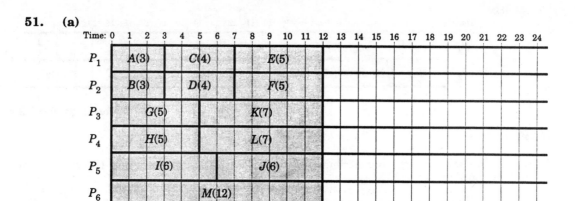

Finishing time = 12

(b)

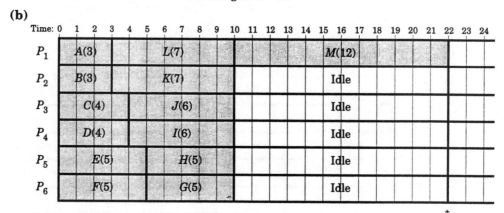

Finishing time = 22

53.   **(a)**

Time: 0	5	10	15	20	25	30	35	40	45	50	55	60	65

P_1: A   F   G   H   I

P_2: D   B   Idle

P_3: E   C   Idle

Finishing time = 65

(b)

Time: 0	5	10	15	20	25	30	35	40	45	50	55	60	65

P_1: A   F   I

P_2: B   G   D

P_3: C   H   E

Finishing time = 45

55. **(a)**

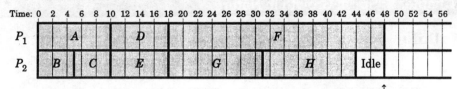

↑
Finishing time = 48

(b)

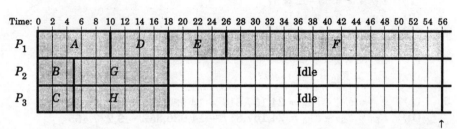

↑
Finishing time = 56

(c) The critical path for this project has length 48 and so the job cannot be completed any sooner. Consequently, the critical path algorithm with 2 processors produced an optimal schedule. With 3 processors the critical path algorithm produced a longer schedule. This paradoxical situation is a consequence of the fact that in the list processing model, a processor cannot choose to be idle if there is a ready task to be executed. In this example tasks D and E need to be completed early so that the long task F can be started, but processor 2 and processor 3 were forced to start tasks G and H and so were not available to start D or E when they were available. We can see from the two schedules that it is the very addition of processor 3 that actually ended up messing up the timing of things.

Walking

1. $F_{15} = 610, F_{16} = 987, F_{17} = 1597, F_{18} = 2584$

3. (a) $F_{10} = 55$
   (b) $F_{10} + 2 = 55 + 2 = 57$
   (c) $F_{10+2} = F_{12} = 144$
   (d) $F_{10} - 8 = 55 - 8 = 47$
   (e) $F_{10-8} = F_2 = 1$
   (f) $3F_4 = 3 \times 3 = 9$
   (g) $F_{3 \times 4} = F_{12} = 144$

5. (a) $F_{38} = F_{37} + F_{36} = 24{,}157{,}817 + 14{,}930{,}352 = 39{,}088{,}169$
   (b) $F_{35} = F_{37} - F_{36} = 24{,}157{,}817 - 14{,}930{,}352 = 9{,}227{,}465$

7. (a) Both equations express the fact that each term of the Fibonacci sequence is equal to the sum of the two preceding terms. However, in the first equation $(F_N = F_{N-1} + F_{N-2})$ we must have $N \geq 3$, whereas in the second equation $(F_{N+2} = F_{N+1} + F_N)$ we must have $N \geq 1$.
   (b) $F_1 = 1, F_2 = 1,$ and $F_N = F_{N-1} + F_{N-2}$ for $N \geq 3$;
        $F_1 = 1, F_2 = 1,$ and $F_{N+2} = F_{N+1} + F_N$ for $N \geq 1$.

9. $N = 12$ and $M = 12$. ($F_{12} = 12^2$)

11. (a) $47 = 13 + 34$ (b) $48 = 1 + 13 + 34$
    (c) $207 = 8 + 55 + 144$ (d) $210 = 3 + 8 + 55 + 144$

13. (a) $(F_1 + F_2 + F_3 + F_4) + 1 = (1 + 1 + 2 + 3) + 1 = 8 = F_6 = F_{4+2}$
    (b) $(F_1 + F_2 + F_3 + F_4 + F_5) + 1 = (1 + 1 + 2 + 3 + 5) + 1 = 13 = F_7 = F_{5+2}$
    (c) $(F_1 + F_2 + F_3 + \cdots + F_{10}) + 1 = (1 + 1 + 2 + 3 + 5 + 8 + 13 + 21 + 34 + 55) + 1 = 144 = F_{12} = F_{10+2}$
    (d) $(F_1 + F_2 + F_3 + \cdots + F_{11}) + 1 =$
         $(1 + 1 + 2 + 3 + 5 + 8 + 13 + 21 + 34 + 55 + 89) + 1 = 233 = F_{13} = F_{11+2}$

15. (a) $2F_{N+2} - F_{N+3} = F_N$
    (b) $2F_{1+2} - F_{1+3} = 2F_3 - F_4 = 2 \cdot 2 - 3 = 1 = F_1$
    (c) $2F_{4+2} - F_{4+3} = 2F_6 - F_7 = 2 \cdot 8 - 13 = 3 = F_4$
    (d) $2F_{8+2} - F_{8+3} = 2F_{10} - F_{11} = 2 \cdot 55 - 89 = 21 = F_8$

17. $x = 1 + \sqrt{2} \approx 2.414, \; x = 1 - \sqrt{2} \approx -0.414$

19. $x = -1, \; x = \dfrac{8}{3} \approx 2.66667$

21. $\dfrac{F_{14}}{F_{13}} = \dfrac{377}{233} \approx 1.6180258, \quad \dfrac{F_{16}}{F_{15}} = \dfrac{987}{610} \approx 1.6180328, \quad \dfrac{F_{18}}{F_{17}} = \dfrac{2584}{1597} \approx 1.6180338.$ These numbers are increasing and getting closer to the golden ratio Φ.

23. (a) True. Two polygons are similar if their corresponding angles are equal and the lengths of their corresponding sides are proportional.
    (b) False. A 10 by 20 rectangle and a 10 by 10 square have all their angles equal, but are not similar since their sides are not proportional.

25.　20 by 30

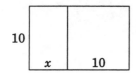

$$\frac{10}{20}=\frac{20}{10+x}$$

$$x=30$$

27.　$c=24$

$$\frac{3}{9}=\frac{9}{c+3}$$

29.　$x=4$

$$\frac{8}{12}=\frac{3+8+1}{2+12+x}\quad\text{i.e.,}\quad\frac{8}{12}=\frac{12}{14+x}$$

31.　$x=12,\,y=10$

$$\frac{3}{4}=\frac{9}{x}\quad\text{and}\quad\frac{3}{5}=\frac{9}{5+y}$$

33.　10 by approximately 6.18

A rectangle with a square gnomon must be a golden rectangle. Therefore

$$\frac{10}{x}=\Phi\quad\text{i.e.,}\quad x=\frac{10}{\Phi}\approx6.18.$$

Jogging

35.　Using the hint, the sum of the two solutions to the equation $x^2-x-1=0$ must be 1. But we know one of the solutions is $\Phi\approx1.618$ and so the other solution must be $1-\Phi$ which is just the negative of the decimal part of Φ.

37.　$x=6,\,y=12,\,z=10$

Since the area of the white triangle is 6, the area of the shaded figure must be 48, which makes the area of the new larger similar triangle 54. Since the ratio of the areas of similar triangles is the square of the ratio of the sides, we have

$$\frac{3+x}{3}=\sqrt{\frac{54}{6}}=3\quad\text{and}\quad\frac{y}{4}=\sqrt{\frac{54}{6}}=3\quad\text{and}\quad\frac{5+z}{5}=\sqrt{\frac{54}{6}}=3.$$

39.　$x=3,\,y=5$

Since the area of the white rectangle is 60 and the area of the shaded figure is 75, the area of the new larger similar rectangle is 135. Since the ratio of the areas of similar rectangles is the square of the ratio of the sides, we have

$$\frac{6+x}{6}=\sqrt{\frac{135}{60}}=\sqrt{\frac{9}{4}}=\frac{3}{2}\quad\text{and}\quad\frac{10+y}{10}=\frac{3}{2}.$$

41.　If　$\Phi^N=a\Phi+b$　then　$\Phi^{N+1}=(a\Phi+b)\Phi=a\Phi^2+b\Phi=a(\Phi+1)+b\Phi=(a+b)\Phi+a$.
　　　(Remember $\Phi^2=\Phi+1$.)

43.　We must have $\dfrac{b+y}{b}=\dfrac{h+x}{h}$ or, equivalently, $1+\dfrac{y}{b}=1+\dfrac{x}{h}$. This gives $\dfrac{y}{b}=\dfrac{x}{h}$ or, equivalently, $\dfrac{y}{x}=\dfrac{b}{h}$.

45. **(a)** Since we are given that $AB = BC = 1$, we know that $\angle BAC = 72°$ and so $\angle BAD = 180° - 72° = 108°$. This makes $\angle ABD = 180° - 108° - 36° = 36°$ and so $\triangle ABD$ is isosceles with $AD = AB = 1$. Therefore $AC = x - 1$. Using these facts and the similarity of $\triangle ACB$ and $\triangle BCD$ we have $\dfrac{x}{1} = \dfrac{1}{x-1}$ or $x^2 = x + 1$ for which we know the solution is $x = \Phi$.

(b) $36°$-$36°$-$108°$

(c) $\dfrac{\text{Longer side}}{\text{Shorter side}} = \dfrac{x}{1} = x = \Phi$

47. $A_N = 5F_N$

49. **(a)** $T_1 = aF_2 + bF_1 = a + b$

(b) $T_2 = aF_3 + bF_2 = 2a + b$

(c) $\begin{aligned} T_N &= aF_{N+1} + bF_N \\ &= a(F_N + F_{N-1}) + b(F_{N-1} + F_{N-2}) \\ &= (aF_N + bF_{N-1}) + (aF_{N-1} + bF_{N-2}) \\ &= T_{N-1} + T_{N-2} \end{aligned}$

51. Follows from Exercise 45 and the following figure.

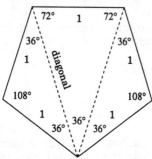

53. From the Pythagorean theorem, $CA^2 = r^2 + (2r)^2 = 5r^2$ and so $CA = r\sqrt{5}$. Therefore,

$$AD = CA - r = r\sqrt{5} - r = r(\sqrt{5} - 1) \text{ and } AP = r\left(\frac{\sqrt{5}-1}{2}\right) = r\left(\frac{\sqrt{5}+1}{2} - 1\right) = r(\Phi - 1) = \frac{r}{\Phi}$$

which is the length of the side of the decagon. The length of the side of the decagon follows from Exercise 45 and the following figure.

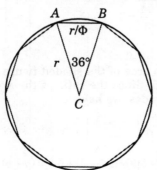

Chapter 10: The Mathematics of Population Growth

Walking

1. **(a)** $P_4 = 26$

   $P_3 = P_2 + P_1 = 10 + 6 = 16; P_4 = P_3 + P_2 = 16 + 10 = 26$.

   (b) $P_6 = 68$

   $P_5 = P_4 + P_3 = 26 + 16 = 42; P_6 = P_5 + P_4 = 42 + 26 = 68$.

   (c) No. The sum of two even numbers is even.

3. **(a)** $P_N = P_{N-1} + 5; P_1 = 3$
   (b) $P_N = 3 + 5(N - 1) = 5N - 2$
   (c) $P_{300} = 3 + 5 \times 299 = 1498$

5. **(a)** $P_2 = 205, P_3 = 330, P_4 = 455$

   $P_2 = P_1 + 125 = 80 + 125 = 205, P_3 = P_2 + 125 = 205 + 125 = 330, P_4 = P_3 + 125 = 330 + 125 = 455$

   (b) $P_{100} = 12{,}455$

   $P_{100} = P_1 + 99 \times 125 = 80 + 12{,}375 = 12{,}455$

   (c) $P_N = 80 + 125(N - 1) = 125N - 45$

7. **(a)** $d = 3$

   $35 = P_{10} = P_1 + 9d = 8 + 9d$ and so $9d = 27$ or $d = 3$.

   (b) $P_{51} = 158$

   $P_{51} = P_1 + 50d = 8 + 50 \times 3 = 158$

   (c) $P_N = 8 + 3(N - 1) = 3N + 5$

9. 24,950

   $P_1 = 2, d = 5, P_{100} = 2 + 99 \times 5 = 497, S_{100} = \dfrac{(2 + 497) \times 100}{2} = 24{,}950$.

11. 16,050

    $P_1 = 12, d = 3, 309 = P_N = 12 + 3(N - 1)$ and so $309 = 12 + 3N - 3$ or $N = 100$,

    $S_{100} = \dfrac{(12 + 309) \times 100}{2} = 16{,}050$.

13. **(a)** 3,519,500

    $P_{1000} = 23 + 999 \times 7 = 7016, P_1 + P_2 + \cdots + P_{1000} = \dfrac{(23 + 7016) \times 1000}{2} = 3{,}519{,}500$.

    (b) 3,482,550

    $P_{100} = 23 + 99 \times 7 = 716, P_1 + P_2 + \cdots + P_{100} = \dfrac{(23 + 716) \times 100}{2} = 36{,}950$,

    $P_{101} + P_{102} + \cdots + P_{1000} = (P_1 + P_2 + \cdots + P_{1000}) - (P_1 + P_2 + \cdots + P_{100}) = 3{,}519{,}500 - 36{,}950 = 3{,}482{,}550$.

15. **(a)** 213

    $137 + 2 \times 38 = 213$

    (b) $137 + 2N$
    (c) $7124

$137 \times 52 = \$7124$

(d) $2652

$$\$(2+4+6+\cdots+102) = \$\frac{(2+102)\times 51}{2} = \$2652$$

17. **(a)** $40.50 **(b)** 40.5% **(c)** 40.5%

Letting P be the marked price, a discount of 15% followed by a discount of 30% results in a price of $0.70(0.85P) = 0.595P$. A discount of 30% followed by a discount of 15% results in a price of $0.85(0.70P) = 0.595P$. In both cases the discounted price is 59.5% of the marked price, a discount of 40.5%.

19. 39.15%

Letting T be the tuition at the beginning of the three-year period, the tuition at the end of the three-year period is $(1.10)(1.15)(1.10)T = 1.3915T$. This is an increase of 39.15%.

21. $4587.64

$\$3250(1.09)^4 \approx \$4587.64$

23. **(a)** $9083.48

$$\$5000\left(1+\frac{0.12}{12}\right)^{12\times 5} = \$5000(1.01)^{60} \approx \$9083.48$$

(b) 12.6825%

$(1.01)^{12} \approx 1.126825$, an annual yield of $1.126825 - 1 = 0.126825 = 12.6825\%$

25. The Great Bulldog Bank: 6%; The First Northern Bank: $\approx 5.9\%$; The Bank of Wonderland: $\approx 5.65\%$.

The First Northern Bank: $\left(1+\dfrac{0.0575}{12}\right)^{12} \approx 1.0590$, an annual yield of 5.90%;

The Bank of Wonderland: $\left(1+\dfrac{0.055}{365}\right)^{365} \approx 1.0565$, an annual yield of 5.65%.

27. $\approx \$1133.56$

$\$100(1.005)^{11} + \$100(1.005)^{10} + \$100(1.005)^9 + \cdots + \$100(1.005) =$
$\$100(1.005) + \$100(1.005)^2 + \$100(1.005)^3 + \cdots + \$100(1.005)^{11} =$
$$\frac{\$100(1.005)(1.005^{11}-1)}{1.005-1} \approx \$1133.56$$

29. **(a)** $6209.21

$$P(1.10)^5 = \$10,000 \text{ and so } P = \frac{\$10,000}{1.10^5} \approx \$6209.21.$$

(b) $6102.71

$$P\left(1+\frac{0.10}{4}\right)^{4\times 5} = \$10,000 \text{ and so } P = \frac{\$10,000}{1.025^{20}} \approx \$6102.71.$$

(c) $6077.89

$$P\left(1+\frac{0.10}{12}\right)^{12\times 5} = \$10,000 \text{ and so } P = \frac{\$10,000}{1.00833333^{60}} \approx \$6077.89.$$

31. (a) $P_2 = 11 \times 1.25 = 13.75$

(b) $P_{10} = 11 \times 1.25^9 \approx 81.956$

(c) $P_N = 11 \times 1.25^{N-1}$

33. (a) $P_{100} = 3 \times 2^{99}$

(b) $P_N = 3 \times 2^{N-1}$

(c) $3 \times (2^{100} - 1)$

$$P_1 + P_2 + \cdots + P_{100} = 3 + 3 \times 2 + 3 \times 2^2 + \cdots + 3 \times 2^{99} = \frac{3 \times (2^{100} - 1)}{2 - 1} = 3 \times (2^{100} - 1)$$

(d) $3 \times 2^{49} \times (2^{51} - 1)$

$$P_{50} + \cdots + P_{100} = 3 \times 2^{49} + 3 \times 2^{50} + \cdots + 3 \times 2^{99} = \frac{3 \times 2^{49} \times (2^{51} - 1)}{2 - 1} = 3 \times 2^{49} \times (2^{51} - 1)$$

35. (a) $p_2 = 0.357$ (b) $p_3 \approx 0.64274$ (c) $p_5 \approx 0.64278$

$p_2 = 2.8 \times (1 - 0.15) \times 0.15 = 0.357$; $p_3 = 2.8 \times (1 - 0.357) \times 0.357 \approx 0.64274$;

$p_4 = 2.8 \times (1 - 0.64274) \times 0.64274 \approx 0.64295$;

$p_5 = 2.8 \times (1 - 0.64295) \times 0.64295 \approx 0.64278$.

37. $p_2 = 0.3825$, $p_3 = 0.70858125$, $p_4 = 0.619481586$, $p_5 \approx 0.707172452$,
$p_6 \approx 0.621238725$, $p_7 \approx 0.705903515$, $p_8 \approx 0.622811228$, $p_9 \approx 0.704752207$,
$p_{10} \approx 0.624229601$ (Answers rounded to 9 decimal places after each transition.)

Jogging

39. 100%

Let C be her cost and x be the markup. Then $0.75(1 + x)C = (1 + 0.50)C$. Dividing both sides of the equation by C and simplifying gives $x = 1 = 100\%$.

41. $10,737,418.23

$1 + 2 + 2^2 + 2^3 + \cdots + 2^{29} = 2^{30} - 1 = 1,073,741,823$ cents, i.e., $10,737,418.23.

43. No. This would require $p_1 = p_2 = 0.8(1 - p_1)p_1$ and so $1 = 0.8(1 - p_1)$ or $p_1 = -\frac{1}{4}$.

45. $\approx 14,619$ snails

$p_1 = \frac{5000}{20,000} = 0.25$; $p_2 = 3.0 \times (1 - 0.25) \times 0.25 = 0.5625$;

$p_3 = 3.0 \times (1 - 0.5625) \times 0.5625 \approx 0.73828$; $p_4 = 3.0 \times (1 - 0.73828) \times 0.73828 \approx 0.57967$;

$p_5 = 3.0 \times (1 - 0.57967) \times 0.57967 \approx 0.73096$; $P_5 \approx 0.73096 \times 20,000 \approx 14,619$.

47. $\approx \$105,006$

$$\$1000 = \frac{B\left(\frac{0.11}{12}\right)\left(1 + \frac{0.11}{12}\right)^{360}}{\left(1 + \frac{0.11}{12}\right)^{360} - 1}; \quad \$1000 = \frac{0.244824B}{25.7081}; \quad B \approx \$105,006.$$

49.   6425

$1+5+3+8+5+11+7+14+\cdots+99+152 =$
$(1+3+5+7+\cdots+99)+(5+8+11+14+\cdots+152) =$
$\dfrac{(1+99)\times 50}{2}+\dfrac{(5+152)\times 50}{2} = 2500+3925 = 6425$

Chapter 11: Symmetry

Walking

1.

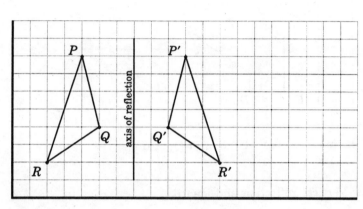

3. **(a)** 140°

500° − 360° = 140°

(b) 279°

3681° − 360 × 10 = 81° clockwise; 360° − 81° = 279° counter-clockwise.

5.

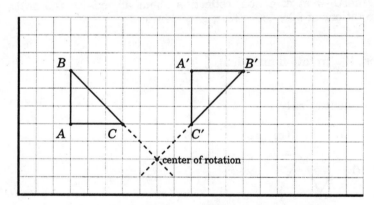

7.

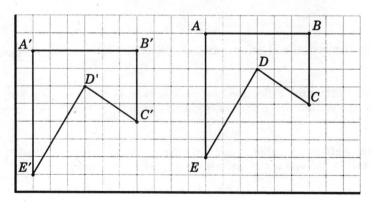

9.

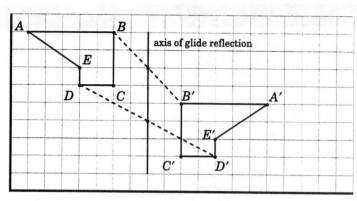

11.   **(a)**   b A T   **(b)**   M I T   **(c)**   b A d   **(d)**   b o Y

13.   **(a)** D_1

Symmetries: Vertical reflection and identity.

   (b) D_1

Symmetries: Horizontal reflection and identity.

   (c) D_4

Symmetries: Horizontal reflection, vertical reflection, reflection about an axis in the north-west direction, reflection about an axis in the north-east direction, rotations of 90°, 180°, 270°, and identity.

   (d) Z_2

Symmetries: 180° rotation and identity.

   (e) Z_1

Symmetries: Identity only.

15.   **(a)**   J   **(b)**   T   **(c)**   S   **(d)**   I   **(e)**   O

17.   **(a)**   **(b)**

19.   **(a)** D_2

Symmetries: Horizontal reflection, vertical reflection; 180° rotation, identity.

   (b) D_4

Symmetries: Horizontal reflection, vertical reflection, reflections about the diagonals of the center white square, rotations of 90°, 180°, 270°, identity.

   (c) D_3

Symmetries: Reflections about any axis that passes through the tips of opposite petals, rotations about the center of 120°, 240°, identity.

   (d) D_8

Symmetries: Reflections about any axis that passes through the tips of opposite petals or between petals, rotations about the center of 45°, 90°, 135°, 180°, 225°, 270°, 315°, identity.

21. **(a)** Translation, vertical reflection, identity.
     (b) Translation, horizontal reflection, identity.
     (c) Translation, 180° rotation, identity.
     (d) Translation, identity.

23. **(a)** Translation, identity.
     (b) Translation, vertical reflection, identity.
     (c) Translation, horizontal reflection, identity.
     (d) Translation, 180° rotation, identity.

25. Since every rigid motion is equivalent to either a reflection, rotation, translation, or glide reflection, and a rotation has only one fixed point while translations and glide reflections have no fixed points, the specified rigid motion must be equivalent to a reflection.

Jogging

27. A reflection is an improper rigid motion and hence reverses the left-right orientation. The propeller blades have a protrusion on the right (as you face the blade) and so after a reflection the protrusion will be on the left.

29. **(a)**

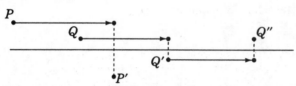

     (b) The result of applying the same glide reflection twice is equivalent to a translation in the direction of the glide of twice the amount of the original glide. [See figure in part (a).]

31. **(a)**

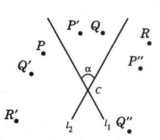

P', Q', and R' are the result of applying reflection 1; P'', Q'', and R'' are the result of applying reflection 2 to P', Q', and R', respectively.

     (b) The result of applying reflection 1 followed by reflection 2 is a clockwise rotation with center C and angle of rotation $\gamma + \gamma + \beta + \beta = 2(\gamma + \beta) = 2\alpha$. (See figure.)

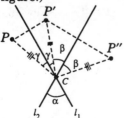

     (c) The result of applying reflection 2 followed by reflection 1 is a counterclockwise rotation with center C and angle 2α.

33. **(a)** By definition, a border pattern has translation symmetries in exactly one direction (let's assume the horizontal direction). If the pattern had a reflection symmetry along an axis forming a 45° angle with the horizontal direction, there would have to be a second direction of translation symmetry (vertical).

(b) If a border pattern had a reflection symmetry along an axis forming an angle of $\alpha°$ with the horizontal direction, it would have to have translation symmetry in a direction that forms an angle of $2\alpha°$ with the horizontal. This could only happen for $\alpha = 90$ or $\alpha = 180$ (since the only allowable direction for translation symmetries is horizontal).

35. **(a)** Translation, 180° rotation, identity.
    (b) Translation, 180° rotation, identity.
    (c) Translation, vertical reflection, 180° rotation, glide reflection, identity.

37. **(a)** Rotations and translations are proper rigid motions, and hence preserve clockwise-counterclockwise orientations. The given motion is an improper rigid motion (it reverses the clockwise-counterclockwise orientation).
    (b) If the rigid motion was a reflection, then PP', RR', and QQ' would all be perpendicular to the axis of reflection and hence would all be parallel.
    (c) It must be a glide reflection (the only rigid motion left).

39. A rotation (see Exercise 31).

41. A glide reflection.

43. Answers will vary.

Chapter 12: Fractal Geometry

Walking

1. **(a), (b), (c)** The line segment joining the midpoints of two sides of a triangle is parallel to the third side and has length one-half the third side. This implies that all the triangles are congruent and therefore the area of each one is $\frac{1}{4}X$.

    (d) $\frac{3}{4}X$. [See (a), (b), (c) above.]

3. **(a)** $\frac{9}{16}X$

    The area of each of the blue triangles in step 1 is $\frac{1}{4}$ the area of $\triangle ABC$, i.e., $\frac{1}{4}X$. The area of each of the blue triangles in step 2 is $\frac{1}{4}$ the area of each of the blue triangles in step 1, i.e., $\frac{1}{4}$ of $\frac{1}{4}X$, or $\frac{1}{16}X$. Since there are 9 blue triangles in step 2, the area of the blue region in step 2 is $\frac{9}{16}X$.

    (b) $\frac{27}{64}X$

    In step 3, each of the blue triangles has area $\frac{1}{4}$ the area of each of the blue triangles in step 2, i.e., $\frac{1}{4}$ of $\frac{1}{16}X$ or $\frac{1}{64}X$. Since there are 3 times as many blue triangles in step 3 as there are in step 2, there are 27 blue triangles in step 3. Therefore the area of the blue region in step 3 is $\frac{27}{64}X$.

    (c) $\left(\frac{3}{4}\right)^N X$

    From parts (a) and (b) we see that at each step we have 3 times as many blue triangles, each of which is $\frac{1}{4}$ the area of a blue triangle in the preceding step. Consequently the total blue area at each step is $\frac{3}{4}$ the blue area in the preceding step.

    (d) $\left(\frac{3}{4}\right)^N$ gets closer and closer to 0 as N gets bigger and bigger.

5. $36 = 6^2$, 6^9, 6^{N-1}

    At each step, each blue triangle is divided into 9 subtriangles of which 3 are removed. Consequently, each blue triangle is replaced by 6 smaller blue triangles. Therefore, there are 6 times as many blue triangles as there were in the preceding step. At the beginning of step 1 there is 1 blue triangle; at the beginning of step 2 there are 6 blue triangles; at the beginning of step 3, $6^2 = 36$; at the beginning of step N, 6^{N-1}.

7. **(a)** $\frac{1}{3}P$ **(b)** $2P$ **(c)** $4P$

    At each step, each blue triangle has perimeter $\frac{1}{3}$ the perimeter of a blue triangle in the preceding step; however, from Exercise 5, there are 6 times as many blue triangles as in the preceding step. Therefore, the perimeter of the blue region at each step is $\frac{6}{3} = 2$ times the perimeter of the blue region in the preceding step.

9.

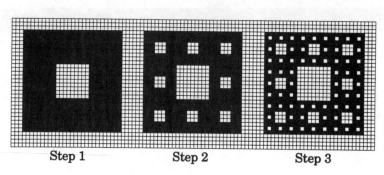

Step 1   Step 2   Step 3

11. **(a)** 512   **(b)** $\left(\frac{8}{9}\right)^3 X = \frac{512}{729} X$ **(c)** 8^N **(d)** $\left(\frac{8}{9}\right)^N X$

At each step, each solid square is divided into 9 subsquares of which 1 is removed. Consequently, each solid square is replaced by 8 smaller solid squares. Therefore, there are 8 times as many solid squares as there were in the preceding step. At the same time, each solid square has area $\frac{1}{9}$ the area of a solid square in the preceding step. Therefore, the area of the solid region at each step is $\frac{8}{9}$ of the area of the solid region in the preceding step.

(e) $\left(\frac{8}{9}\right)^N$ gets closer and closer to 0 as N gets bigger and bigger.

13. Start with a ■. Wherever you see a ———, replace it with a ▁■▁.

15. **(a)** $\frac{20}{3}, \frac{100}{9}$ **(b)** $4\left(\frac{5}{3}\right)^N$

At the start the figure (square) has 4 sides each of length 1 giving a perimeter of 4. At step 1, each of these 4 sides is replaced with 5 new sides, each of these new sides being of length $\frac{1}{3}$. Thus we have $5 \times 4 = 20$ sides, each of length $\frac{1}{3}$, giving a perimeter of $\frac{20}{3}$. At each subsequent step, each of the sides is replaced with 5 new sides and each of these new sides is $\frac{1}{3}$ the length of a side in the preceding step. Consequently, the perimeter at each step is $\frac{5}{3}$ the perimeter at the preceding step.

17.

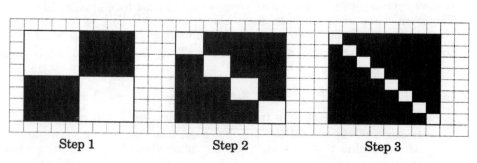

Step 1   Step 2   Step 3

19. $\left[1 - \left(\frac{1}{2}\right)^N\right] X$

At step 1 there are 2 white rectangles, each of area $\frac{1}{4} X$, making the white area $\frac{1}{2} X$ and the colored area $1 - \frac{1}{2} X = \frac{1}{2} X$. At step 2 there are 4 white rectangles, each of area $\frac{1}{16} X$, making the white area $\frac{1}{4} X = \left(\frac{1}{2}\right)^2 X$ and the colored area $\left[1 - \left(\frac{1}{2}\right)^2\right] X$. At each subsequent step, the number of white rectangles doubles while the area of each white rectangle is $\frac{1}{4}$ the area of a white rectangle in the preceding step. Therefore, the total area of the white rectangles at step N is $\left(\frac{1}{2}\right)^N X$ and so the area of the colored region is $\left[1-\left(\frac{1}{2}\right)^N\right]X$.

Note: Another way to solve this problem is to slide the top colored area down, closing up the white rectangles, making a rectangle of area $\left[1-\left(\frac{1}{2}\right)^N\right]X$.

21.

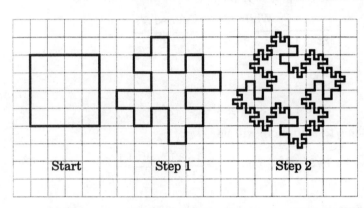

23.   **(a)** $2P, 4P$ **(b)** $2^N P$

This can best be seen by observing that ⌐⌐ is exactly twice as long as ___ .

25.

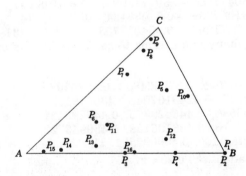

27.

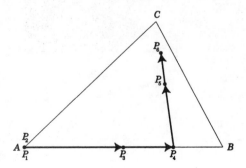

29.   **(a)**   2, 2, 2, 2, 2

Start: -2; Step 1: $(-2)^2 + (-2) = 2$; Step 2: $(2)^2 + (-2) = 2$; . . .

Step 5: $(2)^2 + (-2) = 2$.

  (b)   attracted

Jogging

31.   At each step, one new white triangle is introduced for each colored triangle and the number of colored triangles is tripled.

	White Δ's	Colored Δ's
Step 1	1	3
Step 2	$1+3$	3^2
Step 3	$1+3+3^2$	3^3
Step 4	$1+3+3^2+3^3$	3^4

We see that at the Nth step there will be

$$1+3+3^2+3^3+\cdots+3^{N-1} = \frac{1-3^N}{1-3} = \frac{3^N-1}{2}$$

white triangles.

33.   There will be infinitely many points left. For example, the 3 vertices of the original triangle will be left as well as the vertices of every colored triangle that occurs at each step of the construction.

35. -0.1875, -0.71484375, -0.238998413, -0.692879759, -0.26991764, -0.677144468, -0.29147537, -0.665042109, -0.307718994, -0.655309021, -0.320570087, -0.647234819, -0.331087089, -0.64038134, -0.33991174, -0.634460009, -0.347460497, -0.629271203, -0.354017753, -0.624671431

Attracted to -0.5 (although it takes many more terms to see this). This is one of the solutions of the equation $x^2 - 0.75 = x$.

37.   The first twenty steps: 0.3125, 0.34765625, 0.370864868, 0.38754075, 0.400187833, 0.410150302, 0.41822327, 0.424910704, 0.430549106, 0.435372533, 0.439549242, 0.443203536, 0.446429375, 0.449299187, 0.451869759, 0.454186279, 0.456285176, 0.458196162, 0.459943723, 0.461548228. Step 99: 0.49060422; step 100: 0.490692501. This sequence is attracted to 0.5, a solution of the equation $x^2 + 0.25 = x$.

39.   Step 1: $2 + \sqrt{2}$. This sequence is escaping.

Chapter 13: Collecting Statistical Data

Walking

1. **(a)** Answer 1: All married people. Answer 2: All married people who read Dear Abby's column. Note: While both answers are acceptable, it is clear that Dear Abby was trying to draw conclusions about married people at large so answer 1 is better. Also note that from the wording of her conclusion ("... there are far more faithfully wed couples than I had surmised") one can assume that she was primarily interested in currently married people as opposed to divorcees, widows and widowers.
    (b) 210,336
    (c) self-selection
    (d) 85% is a statistic, since it is based on data taken from a sample.

3. **(a)** 74.0%
    (b) 81.8%
    (c) Not very accurate. The sample was far from being representative of the entire population.

5. **(a)** The citizens of Cleansburg.
    (b) 475

7. **(a)** The choice of street corner could make a great deal of difference in the responses collected.
    (b) *D*. (We are making the assumption that people who live or work downtown are much more likely to answer yes than people in other parts of town.)
    (c) Yes, for two main reasons: (i) people out on the street between 4 P.M. and 6 P.M. are not representative of the population at large. For example, office and white collar workers are much more likely to be in the sample than homemakers and school teachers. (ii) The five street corners were chosen by the interviewers and the passersby are unlikely to represent a cross section of the city.
    (d) No. No attempt was made to use quotas to get a representative cross section of the population.

9. **(a)** All undergraduates at Tasmania State University.
    (b) $N = 15,000$

11. **(a)** No. The sample was chosen by a random method.
    (b) In simple random sampling, any two members of the population have as much chance of both being in the sample as any other two. But in this sample, two people with the same last name—say Len Euler and Linda Euler—have no chance of both being in the sample. (By the way, the sampling method described in this exercise is frequently used and goes by the technical name of **systematic sampling**.)

13. **(a)** Anyone who could have a cold and would consider buying vitamin *X* (i.e., pretty much all adults).
    (b) Presumably they volunteered. (We could infer this from the fact that they are being paid.)
    (c) $n = 500$
    (d) No. There was no control group.

15. ■ Using college students. (College students are not a representative cross section of the population in terms of age and therefore in terms of how they would respond to the treatment.)
    ■ Using subjects only from the San Diego area.
    ■ Offering money as an incentive to participate.

■ Allowing self-reporting (the subjects themselves determine when their colds are over) is a very unreliable way to collect data and is especially bad when the subjects are paid volunteers.

17. Anyone who could potentially suffer from arteriosclerosis (clogging of the arteries).

19. **(a)** There was a treatment group (the ones getting the beta-carotene pill) and there was a control group. The control group received a placebo pill. These two elements make it a controlled placebo experiment.
(b) The group that received the beta-carotene pills.
(c) Both the treatment and control groups were chosen by random selection.

21. The professor was conducting a clinical study because he was, after all, trying to establish the connection between a cause (10 milligrams of caffeine a day) and an effect (improved performance in college courses). Other than that, the experiment had little going for it: it was not controlled (no control group); not randomized (the subjects were chosen because of their poor grades); no placebo was used and consequently the study was not double-blind.

23. **(i)** A regular visit to the professor's office could in itself be a boost to a student's self-confidence and help improve his or her grades.
(ii) The "individualized tutoring" that took place during the office meetings could also be the reason for improved performance.
(iii) The students selected for the study all got F's on their first midterm making them likely candidates to show some improvement.

Jogging

25. **(a)** (i) the entire sky; (ii) all the coffee in the cup; (iii) all the blood in Carla's body.
(b) In none of the three examples is the sample random.
(c) (i) In some situations one can have a good idea as to whether it will rain or not by seeing only a small section of the sky, but in many other situations rain clouds can be patchy and one might draw the wrong conclusions by just peeking out the window. (ii) If the coffee is burning hot on top, it is likely to be pretty hot throughout, so Betty's conclusion is likely to be valid. (iii) Because of the constant circulation of blood in our system, the 5 ml. of blood drawn out of Carla's right arm is representative of all the blood in her body, so the lab's results are very likely to be valid.

27. **(a)** The question was worded in a way that made it almost impossible to answer yes.
(b) "Will you support some form of tax increase if it can be proven to you that such a tax increase is justified?" is better, but still not neutral. "Do you support or oppose some form of tax increase?" is bland but probably as neutral as one can get.

29. **(a)** Under method 1, people whose phone numbers are unlisted are automatically ruled out from the sample. At the same time, method 1 is cheaper and easier to implement than method 2.
(b) For this particular situation, method 2 is likely to produce much more reliable data than method 1. The two main reasons are: (i) People with unlisted phone numbers are very likely to be the same kind of people that would seriously consider buying a burglar alarm, and (ii) the listing bias is more likely to be significant in a place like New York City. (People with unlisted phone numbers make up a much higher percentage of the population in a large city such as New York than in a small town or rural area. Interestingly enough, the largest percentage of unlisted phone numbers for any American city is in Las Vegas, Nevada.)

31. **(a)** 2000

$$N = \frac{n_2}{k} \cdot n_1 = \frac{120}{30} \times 500 = 2000$$

(e) 20,500

$$N = \frac{n_2}{k} \cdot n_1 = \frac{900}{218} \times 4965 \approx 20,497.7 \approx 20,500$$

33. **(a)** Issue 1. Who should be getting the treatment? (Individuals who are HIV positive but otherwise appear healthy? Individuals who are already at a very advanced stage of the AIDS disease? Those in between? Some of each group? How about money? (Should anyone who can afford the treatment be allowed to get it?)

Issue 2. Is the remedy worse than the disease? How serious are the possible side effects in humans? (The drug has been tested only on laboratory animals.) Who should be making the decision as to whether the risks justify the benefits? (Patient? Doctor? Insurance Company?)

Issue 3. Should there be a placebo group? (In matters of life and death is it fair to tell a patient that he/she may be getting a "fake" treatment?)

(b) This is an open ended question and appropriate for class discussion and/or a report. At present, there are no well established protocols for dealing with some of these issues.

Chapter 14: Descriptive Statistics

Walking

1. **(a)**

Score	10	50	60	70	80	100
Frequency	1	3	7	6	5	2

(b)

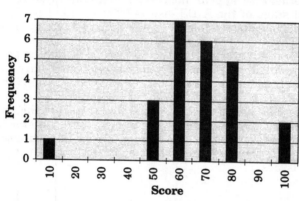

(c)

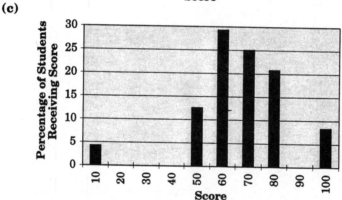

3. **(a)** Min = 10, $Q_1 = 60$, $M = 70$, $Q_3 = 80$, Max = 100

$$Q_1 = \frac{60+60}{2} = 60 \quad M = Q_2 = \frac{70+70}{2} = 70 \quad Q_3 = \frac{80+80}{2} = 80$$

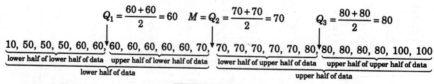

10, 50, 50, 50, 60, 60, | 60, 60, 60, 60, 60, 70, | 70, 70, 70, 70, 70, 80, | 80, 80, 80, 80, 100, 100

lower half of lower half of data   upper half of lower half of data   lower half of upper half of data   upper half of upper half of data

lower half of data   upper half of data

(b)

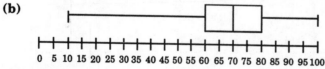

0   5 10 15 20 25 30 35 40 45 50 55 60 65 70 75 80 85 90 95 100

5. **(a)** 65.32%   **(b)** 70%   **(c)** $Q_1 = 55\%$, $Q_3 = 76\%$ **(d)** IQR = 21%

Average =

$$\frac{92 + 2 \times 83 + 78 + 2 \times 77 + 76 + 75 + 3 \times 74 + 3 \times 70 + 59 + 2 \times 57 + 56 + 3 \times 55 + 52 + 51 + 50 + 13}{25} =$$

$$\frac{1633}{25} = 65.32$$

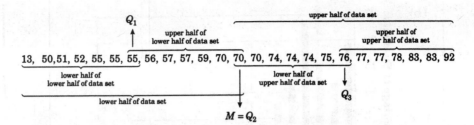

13, 50, 51, 52, 55, 55, 55, 56, 57, 57, 59, 70, 70, 70, 74, 74, 74, 75, 76, 77, 77, 78, 83, 83, 92

7. **(a)**   ≈ 248.38   **(b)**   ≈ 15.76%

$$\text{Variance} = \big[(13-65.32)^2 + (50-65.32)^2 + (51-65.32)^2 + (52-65.32)^2 +$$
$$3 \times (55-65.32)^2 + (56-65.32)^2 + 2 \times (57-65.32)^2 + (59-65.32)^2 +$$
$$3 \times (70-65.32)^2 + 3 \times (74-65.32)^2 + (75-65.32)^2 + (76-65.32)^2 +$$
$$2 \times (77-65.32)^2 + (78-65.32)^2 + 2 \times (83-65.32)^2 + (92-65.32)^2\big] / 25 \approx$$
$$\frac{6209.44}{25} \approx 248.38$$
$$\text{SD} \approx \sqrt{248.38} \approx 15.76$$

9.

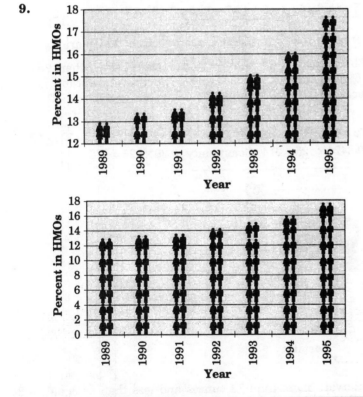

11. **(a)**

Distance to School (miles)	0.0	0.5	1.0	1.5	2.0	2.5	3.0	5.0	8.5
Frequency	5	3	4	6	3	2	1	1	1

(b)

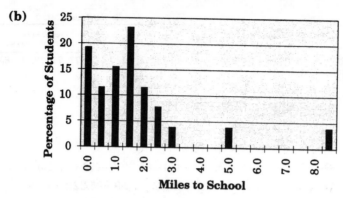

13. **(a)** 30

(b)

Score	3	4	5	6	7	8	9	10
Frequency	2	5	6	4	4	5	3	1

(c) 6.17   **(d)** 6

$$\text{Average} = \frac{2 \times 3 + 5 \times 4 + 6 \times 5 + 4 \times 6 + 4 \times 7 + 5 \times 8 + 3 \times 9 + 10}{30} = \frac{185}{30} \approx 6.17;$$

Median is the average of the 15th and 16th score, both of which are 6.

15. Asian: 40°; Hispanic: 68°; African American: 86°; Caucasian: 140°; Other: 25°.
Asian: $0.11 \times 360° = 39.6°$; Hispanic: $0.19 \times 360° = 68.4°$; African American:
$0.24 \times 360° = 86.4°$; Caucasian: $0.39 \times 360° = 140.4°$; Other: $0.07 \times 360° = 25.2°$.

17. **(a)** 132   **(b)** 9

Downtown : $0.2112 \times 625 = 132$; Other : $0.0144 \times 625 = 9$; County : 0.1520×625
$= 95$; St. Mary's : $0.3424 \times 625 = 214$; Community : $0.28 \times 625 = 175$.

(c)

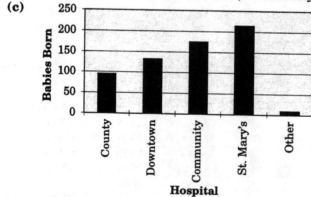

19. **(a)** 12 ounces
(b) The third class interval: "more than 72 ounces and less than or equal to 84
ounces." Values that fall exactly on the boundary between two class
intervals belong to the class interval to the left.

21.

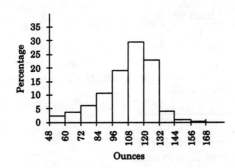

23. Average = 5, SD = 0; Average = 5, SD ≈ 3.54; Average = 5, SD ≈ 11.73.
The averages are all the same but the standard deviations get larger as the numbers are more spread out.

25. **(a)** 4.5   **(b)** 4.5   **(c)** 2   **(d)** 7   **(e)** 5   **(f)** ≈ 2.87

$$\text{Average} = \frac{0+1+2+\cdots+9}{10} = \frac{9 \times 10}{2 \times 10} = 4.5$$

Q_1

$$0, 1, 2, 3, 4, \underbrace{\overbrace{5, 6, 7, 8, 9}^{\text{upper half}}}_{} \qquad M = Q_2 = \frac{4+5}{2} = 4.5$$

lower half

Q_3

$$\text{SD} = \sqrt{\frac{(0-4.5)^2 + (1-4.5)^2 + (2-4.5)^2 + \cdots + (9-4.5)^2}{10}} \approx 2.87$$

27. **(a)** 50.5   **(b)** 50.5

$$\text{Average} = \frac{1+2+\cdots+99+100}{100} = \frac{100 \times 101}{2 \times 100} = 50.5$$

The median is the average of the 50th and 51st terms.

29. **(a)** Min = 9, Q_1 = 13, M = 16, Q_3 = 18, Max = 25. Average ≈ 15.49; standard deviation ≈ 3.11.

Value (V)	Freq (f)	$f \times V$	$V - A$	$(V-A)^2$	$f \times (V-A)^2$
9	3	27	−6.49	42.12	126.36
10	5	50	−5.49	30.14	150.70
11	7	77	−4.49	20.16	141.12
12	4	48	−3.49	12.18	48.72
13	12	156	−2.49	6.20	74.40
14	10	140	−1.49	2.22	22.20
15	13	195	−0.49	0.24	3.12
16	11	176	0.51	0.26	2.86
17	15	255	1.51	2.28	34.20
18	13	234	2.51	6.30	81.90
19	11	209	3.51	12.32	135.52
20	4	80	4.51	20.34	81.36
21	3	63	5.51	30.36	91.08
25	1	25	9.51	90.44	90.44
TOTALS	112	1735			1083.98

Average $(A) = \dfrac{1735}{112} \approx 15.49$; SD $\approx \sqrt{\dfrac{1083.98}{112}} \approx \sqrt{9.68} \approx 3.11$

Since there are 112 scores, the median is the average of the 56th and 57th scores, both of which are 16. The first quartile is the average of the 28th and 29th scores, both of which are 13. The third quartile is the average of the 84th and 85th scores, both of which are 18.

(b)

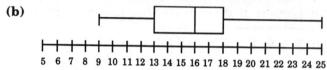

5 6 7 8 9 10 11 12 13 14 15 16 17 18 19 20 21 22 23 24 25

31. (a) 1.5

Average $= \dfrac{2.2 + (-1.1) + (-2.7) + 4.4 + 6.2 + (-2.4) + 3.8 + 1.6}{8} = \dfrac{12}{8} = 1.5$

(b) {0.7, −2.6, −4.2, 2.9, 4.7, −3.9, 2.3, 0.1}

(c) 0

33. (a) 459

$35,000 is the first quartile of engineering salaries, so $0.75 \times 612 = 459$ engineering majors made $35,000 or more.

(b) 240

$25,000 is the first quartile of agriculture salaries, so $0.25 \times 960 = 240$ agriculture majors made $25,000 or less. Note that the exact number that made strictly less than $25,000 cannot be determined from the given information.

35. 58 points

The lowest possible score on the first exam is when all the rest of the scores are as high as possible: $\dfrac{x + 100 + 100 + 100 + 200}{6} = 93$; $x = 558 - 500 = 58$.

Jogging

37. An example is Ramon gets 85 out of 100 on each of the first four exams and 60 out of 100 on the fifth exam while Josh gets 80 out of 100 on all 5 of the exams.

39. (a) {1, 1, 1, 1, 6, 6, 6, 6, 6, 6} Average = 4; Median = 6.

(b) {1, 1, 1, 1, 1, 1, 6, 6, 6, 6} Average = 3; Median = 1.

(c) {1, 1, 6, 6, 6, 6, 6, 6, 6, 6} Average = 5; $Q_1 = 6$.

(d) {1, 1, 1, 1, 1, 1, 1, 1, 6, 6} Average = 2; $Q_3 = 1$.

41. (a) The five-number summary for the original scores was Min = 1, $Q_1 = 9$, $M =$ 11, $Q_3 = 12$, and Max = 24. When 2 points are added to each test score, the five-number summary will also have 2 points added to each of its numbers (i.e., Min = 3, $Q_1 = 11$, $M = 13$, $Q_3 = 14$, and Max = 26).

(b) When 10% is added to each score (i.e., each score is multiplied by 1.1) then each number in the five-number summary will also be multiplied by 1.1 (i.e., Min = 1.1, $Q_1 = 9.9$, $M = 12.1$, $Q_3 = 13.2$, and Max = 26.4).

43. (a) 4

$\dfrac{\text{Column area over interval } 30\text{-}35}{\text{Column area over interval } 20\text{-}30} = \dfrac{5 \times h}{10 \times 1} = \dfrac{50\%}{25\%}$ and so $5h = 20$, $h = 4$.

(b) 0.4

$\dfrac{\text{Column area over interval } 35\text{-}45}{\text{Column area over interval } 20\text{-}30} = \dfrac{10 \times h}{10 \times 1} = \dfrac{10\%}{25\%}$ and so $h = 0.4$.

(c) 0.4

$$\frac{\text{Column area over interval } 45\text{-}60}{\text{Column area over interval } 20\text{-}30} = \frac{15 \times h}{10 \times 1} = \frac{15\%}{25\%} \text{ and so } h = 0.4.$$

45. (a) 10%, 20%   **(b)** 80%, 90%

(c) The figures for both schools were combined. A total of 820 males were admitted out of a total of 1200 that applied — giving approximately 68.3% of the total number of males that applied were admitted. Similarly, a total of 460 females were admitted out of a total of 900 that applied — giving approximately 51.1% of the total number of females that applied were admitted.

(d) In this example, females have a higher percentage ($\frac{100}{500} = 20\%$) than males ($\frac{20}{200} = 10\%$) for admissions to the School of Architecture and also a higher percentage ($\frac{360}{400} = 90\%$) than males ($\frac{800}{1000} = 80\%$) for admissions to the School of Engineering. When the numbers are combined, however, females have a lower percentage ($\frac{100+360}{500+400} \approx 51.1\%$) than males ($\frac{20+800}{200+1000} \approx 68.3\%$) in total admissions. The reason that this apparent paradox can occur is purely a matter of arithmetic: Just because $\frac{a_1}{a_2} > \frac{b_1}{b_2}$ and $\frac{c_1}{c_2} > \frac{d_1}{d_2}$ it does not necessarily follow that $\frac{a_1+c_1}{a_2+c_2} > \frac{b_1+d_1}{b_2+d_2}$.

47. Consider a data set $\{x_1, x_2, x_3, \ldots, x_N\}$ and assume $\text{Min} = x_1 \leq x_2 \leq x_3 \leq \ldots \leq x_N = \text{Max}$. Then since the average A satisfies the inequality $\text{Min} \leq A \leq \text{Max}$, we see that $(x_k - A)^2 \leq (\text{Max} - \text{Min})^2 = \text{Range}^2$ for each $k = 1, 2, 3, \ldots, N$. Therefore,

$$\text{SD} = \sqrt{\frac{(x_1 - A)^2 + (x_2 - A)^2 + \cdots + (x_N - A)^2}{N}} \leq \sqrt{\frac{N \times \text{Range}^2}{N}} = \text{Range}.$$

Chapter 15: Chances, Probability, and Odds

Walking

1. **(a)** {HHHH, HHHT, HHTH, HHTT, HTHH, HTHT, HTTH, HTTT, THHH, THHT, THTH, THTT, TTHH, TTHT, TTTH, TTTT}
  (b) 16
  (c) {HHTT, HTHT, HTTH, THHT, THTH, TTHH}
  (d) $\frac{6}{16} = \frac{3}{8}$

3. **(a)** $\{P_1, P_2, P_3, P_4, P_5, P_6, P_7\}$; $\Pr(P_1) = \frac{1}{4}$; $\Pr(P_2) = \Pr(P_3) = \Pr(P_4) = \Pr(P_5)$ $= \Pr(P_6) = \Pr(P_7) = \frac{1}{8}$.
  Let $x = \Pr(P_2) = \Pr(P_3) = \Pr(P_4) = \Pr(P_5) = \Pr(P_6) = \Pr(P_7)$. Then $2x = \Pr(P_1)$ and so $2x + 6x = 1$, $8x = 1$, $x = \frac{1}{8}$.
  (b) The odds for P_1 winning the tournament are 1 to 3.
  The odds for P_2 winning the tournament are 1 to 7.

5. **(a)** 17,576,000   **(b)** 15,818,400   **(c)** 11,232,000
  $26 \times 26 \times 26 \times 10 \times 10 \times 10 = 17,576,000$
  $26 \times 26 \times 26 \times 9 \times 10 \times 10 = 15,818,400$
  $26 \times 25 \times 24 \times 10 \times 9 \times 8 = 11,232,000$

7. **(a)** 40,320   **(b)** 40,319
  $8! = 8 \times 7 \times 6 \times 5 \times 4 \times 3 \times 2 \times 1 = 40,320$
  The books will be out of order in every arrangement except 1, i.e., $40,320 - 1 = 40,319$.

9. **(a)** {red, blue, yellow, purple, orange}
  (b) {red, blue, yellow}
  (c) {purple, orange}
  (d) $\Pr(\text{red}) = \Pr(\text{blue}) = \Pr(\text{yellow}) = 0.1$; $\Pr(\text{purple}) = \Pr(\text{orange}) = 0.35$

11. { }, {A}, {B}, {C}, {A, B}, {A, C}, {B, C}, {A, B, C}

13. **(a)** $\frac{1}{12}$ **(b)** $\frac{11}{12}$ **(c)** 1 to 11   **(d)** 11 to 1
  There are 3 ways the sum of 10 can be made, {⚃⚅, ⚄⚄, ⚅⚃}. Thus the probability that the sum is 10 is $\frac{3}{36} = \frac{1}{12}$. The probability of not rolling the sum of 10 is $1 - \frac{1}{12} = \frac{11}{12}$. The odds in favor of rolling the sum of 10 are 1 to $(12 - 1)$, i.e., 1 to 11. The odds against rolling the sum of 10 are 11 to 1.

15. **(a)** $E = \{$⚀⚁, ⚀⚃, ⚀⚄, ⚀⚅, ⚁⚃, ⚁⚄, ⚁⚅, ⚂⚄, ⚂⚅, ⚃⚅$\}$
  (b) $\frac{10}{36} = \frac{5}{18}$ **(c)** 5 to 13

17. **(a)** $\frac{1}{36}$ **(b)** $\frac{25}{36}$ **(c)** $\frac{5}{18}$
  Since there are 6 ways (out of 36) for the sum to be 7, $\Pr(\text{"rolling a sum of 7"}) = \frac{6}{36} = \frac{1}{6}$ and so $\Pr(\text{"not rolling a sum of 7"}) = 1 - \frac{1}{6} = \frac{5}{6}$. Therefore, $\Pr(\text{"rolling a 7 in both rolls"}) = \frac{1}{6} \times \frac{1}{6} = \frac{1}{36}$; $\Pr(\text{"not rolling a 7 in either roll"}) = \frac{5}{6} \times \frac{5}{6} = \frac{25}{36}$; $\Pr(\text{"rolling a 7 in one roll and not a 7 in the other"}) = 1 - \frac{1}{36} - \frac{25}{36} = \frac{10}{36} = \frac{5}{18}$.

19. **(a)** $\frac{7}{8}$ **(b)** $\frac{1023}{1024}$
  $\Pr(\text{"getting at least one } H\text{"}) = 1 - \Pr(\text{"getting no } H\text{'s"})$. Therefore, $\Pr(\text{"getting at least one } H \text{ in 3 tosses"}) = 1 - \Pr(TTT) = 1 - \left(\frac{1}{2}\right)^3 = 1 - \frac{1}{8} = \frac{7}{8}$; $\Pr(\text{"getting at}$

least one H in 10 tosses") $= 1 - \Pr(TTTTTTTTTT) = 1 - \left(\frac{1}{2}\right)^{10} = 1 - \frac{1}{1024} = \frac{1023}{1024}$.

21. (a) $\frac{1}{3}$ (b) $\frac{1}{2}$

The sample space for the Greens' children is: $\{BB, BG, GB\}$ where, for example, BG stands for the first (older) child is a boy and the second (younger) child is a girl. Therefore the probability that the Greens have 2 boys is $\frac{1}{3}$. The sample space for the Browns' children is: $\{BB, BG\}$ and so the probability that the Browns have 2 boys is $\frac{1}{2}$.

23. 1320

$12 \times 11 \times 10 = 1320$

25. 364

$_{14}C_3 = \frac{14 \times 13 \times 12}{3 \times 2 \times 1} = 364$

27. 793

$_{13}C_2 = \frac{13 \times 12}{2} = 78$ delegations with Anna and Bob in them; $_{13}C_4 = \frac{13 \times 12 \times 11 \times 10}{4 \times 3 \times 2 \times 1} = 715$ dele-gations without Anna and Bob.

Jogging

29. (a) $\frac{99}{512} \approx 0.19$ (b) $\frac{231}{1024} \approx 0.225$ (c) $\frac{99}{512} \approx 0.19$

$\frac{_{12}C_5}{2^{12}} = \frac{\frac{12 \times 11 \times 10 \times 9 \times 8}{5 \times 4 \times 3 \times 2 \times 1}}{4096} = \frac{792}{4096} = \frac{99}{512} \approx 0.19$ (the $_{12}C_5$ counts the number of ways we can choose the 5 "slots" for the H's);

$\frac{_{12}C_6}{2^{12}} = \frac{\frac{12 \times 11 \times 10 \times 9 \times 8 \times 7}{6 \times 5 \times 4 \times 3 \times 2 \times 1}}{4096} = \frac{924}{4096} = \frac{231}{1024} \approx 0.226$;

The answer to (c) is the same as the answer to (a) (by symmetry—count the number of ways we can choose the 5 "slots" for the T's instead).

31. $\frac{253}{4998} \approx 0.05$

$\frac{2 \times {}_{26}C_5}{2,598,960} = \frac{2 \times \left(\frac{26 \times 25 \times 24 \times 23 \times 22}{5 \times 4 \times 3 \times 2 \times 1}\right)}{2,598,960} = \frac{253}{4998} \approx 0.05$. The denominator is the total number of unordered draw poker hands [see Example 16(b)]. The numerator represents: 2 ways to choose the color $\times$ the number of (unordered) ways to choose 5 cards from the 26 cards of the chosen color.

33. $\frac{1}{2548} \approx 0.00039$

There are 4 ways to choose the 10, 4 ways to choose the J, 4 ways to choose the Q, etc., so there are $4^5 = 1024$ ways to choose a hand consisting of 10, J, Q, K, A. But one of these 1024 hands consists only of hearts, another only of diamonds, another only of clubs, and another only of spades. Therefore there are only 1020 ace-high straights. Consequently, the probability of getting an ace-high straight is $\frac{1020}{2,598,960} = \frac{1}{2548} \approx 0.00039$.

35. 252

This is the same as choosing 5 students from the 10 for the first group and then the remaining students will form the second group, $_{10}C_5 = \frac{10 \times 9 \times 8 \times 7 \times 6}{5 \times 4 \times 3 \times 2 \times 1} = 252$.

37. 20

Each walk is a sequence of six letters, 3 of which are R's (move right) and the other 3 are U's (move up). There are $_6C_3 = \frac{6 \times 5 \times 4}{3 \times 2 \times 1} = 20$ such sequences (we just have to count the number of ways of choosing the 3 slots out of the 6 for the R's).

39. $1 - \left(\frac{5}{6}\right)^5 \approx 0.6$

On each roll, the probability of not rolling a total of 7 is $\frac{30}{36} = \frac{5}{6}$, so the probability of not rolling a total of 7 at all in the 5 rolls of the dice is $\left(\frac{5}{6}\right)^5$. Therefore, the probability of rolling a total of 7 at least once is $1 - \left(\frac{5}{6}\right)^5 \approx 0.6$.

41. $\frac{4}{9}$

Pr(rolling a 2, 3, 4, 9, 10, 11, or 12) $= \frac{1}{36} + \frac{2}{36} + \frac{3}{36} + \frac{4}{36} + \frac{3}{36} + \frac{2}{36} + \frac{1}{36} = \frac{16}{36} = \frac{4}{9}$

43. **(a)** 3,628,800

$_{10}P_{10} = 10! = 10 \times 9 \times 8 \times 7 \times 6 \times 5 \times 4 \times 3 \times 2 \times 1 = 3,628,800$

(b) 362,880

There are 10 different ways to take the same circle of 10 people and break it up into a straight line. It follows that the answer to part (a) is 10 times the answer to part (b).

Chapter 16: Normal Distributions

Walking

1. **(a)** 2   **(b)** 1.4   **(c)** 2.6   **(d)** 0.8

$$\frac{75-45}{15}=2; \quad \frac{51-30}{15}=1.4; \quad \frac{89-50}{15}=2.6; \quad \frac{32-20}{15}=0.8.$$

3. **(a)** 1   **(b)** 1.6   **(c)** −2.0   **(d)** −1.8

$$\frac{45-30}{15}=1; \quad \frac{54-30}{15}=1.6; \quad \frac{0-30}{15}=-2.0; \quad \frac{3-30}{15}=-1.8.$$

5. **(a)** 52   **(b)** 50%   **(c)** 68%   **(d)** 16%

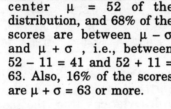

For normally distributed scores, the average is the center $\mu = 52$ of the distribution, and 68% of the scores are between $\mu - \sigma$ and $\mu + \sigma$, i.e., between $52 - 11 = 41$ and $52 + 11 = 63$. Also, 16% of the scores are $\mu + \sigma = 63$ or more.

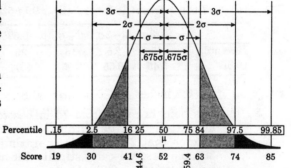

Figure for Exercises 5 through 8.

7. **(a)** 44.6
   (b) 59.4
   (c) 14.8

$$Q_1 \approx \mu - 0.675\sigma \approx 44.6; \quad Q_3 \approx \mu + 0.675\sigma \approx 59.4; \quad IQR \approx 59.4 - 44.6 = 14.8.$$

9. **(a)** 1900   **(b)** 50

11. **(a)** approximately the 3rd percentile
    (b) the 16th percentile
    (c) around the 22nd or 23rd percentile
    (d) the 84th percentile
    (e) the 99.85th percentile

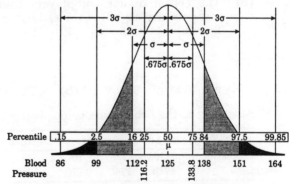

Figure for Exercises 9 through 12.

13. **(a)** 95%
    (b) 47.5%
    (c) 97.5%

15. **(a)** 13   **(b)** 80
    (c) 250   **(d)** 420
    (e) 488   **(f)** 499

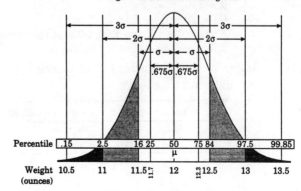

Figure for Exercises 13 through 16.

17. $\mu = 75$, $\sigma = 3$

P and P' are located 1 standard deviation on each side of the mean (average).

19. $\mu = 80$, $\sigma = 10$

Fifty percent of the area is between the 1st and 3rd quartiles, so $\mu - 0.675\sigma = 73.25$ and $\mu + 0.675\sigma = 86.75$. Solving these equations simultaneously gives $\mu = 80$ and $\sigma = 10$.

21. **(a)**   16th percentile   **(b)**   97.5th percentile   **(c)**   18.6 lbs

	$\mu-3\sigma$	$\mu-2\sigma$	$\mu-\sigma$	$\mu-0.675\sigma$	μ	$\mu+0.675\sigma$	$\mu+\sigma$	$\mu+2\sigma$	$\mu+3\sigma$
Percentile	0.15	2.5	16	25	50	75	84	97.5	99.85
Data	11.25	13.25	15.25	15.90	17.25	18.60	19.25	21.25	23.25

23. **(a)**   97.5th percentile   **(b)**   99.85th percentile   **(c)**   8 lbs

	$\mu-3\sigma$	$\mu-2\sigma$	$\mu-\sigma$	$\mu-0.675\sigma$	μ	$\mu+0.675\sigma$	$\mu+\sigma$	$\mu+2\sigma$	$\mu+3\sigma$
Percentile	.15	2.5	16	25	50	75	84	97.5	99.85
Data	5.45	6.55	7.65	8.01	8.75	9.49	9.85	10.95	12.05

25. **(a)** $\sigma \approx 3.5$ inches   **(b)**   6-8   **(c)**   366

The heights range from 70 inches to 91 inches, a range of 21 inches. Since almost all data lie within 3 standard deviations from the mean, we can assume that 21 inches is approximately 6σ, and so $\sigma \approx 3.5$. Since there are 385 players, we can estimate the mean to be the median, i.e., the 193rd height (which is 6-8). Ninety-five percent of the data fall between 2 standard deviations below and above the mean, so approximately $0.95 \times 385 \approx 366$ players' heights are predicted to fall in this range.

(d)   The actual number of players that fall within ±7 inches (2 estimated standard deviations) of the estimated mean (6-8) is 13 + 15 + 22 + 24 + 25 + 29 + 39 + 44 + 45 + 44 + 30 + 21 + 6 + 5 + 2 = 364.

Jogging

27. **(a)** $\mu = 1800$, $\sigma = 30$ **(b)**   68%   **(c)**   34%   **(d)**   13.5%

According to the honest coin principle $\mu = 3600/2 = 1800$ and $\sigma = \sqrt{3600}/2 = 30$.

	$\mu-3\sigma$	$\mu-2\sigma$	$\mu-\sigma$	$\mu-0.675\sigma$	μ	$\mu+0.675\sigma$	$\mu+\sigma$	$\mu+2\sigma$	$\mu+3\sigma$
Percentile	0.15	2.5	16	25	50	75	84	97.5	99.85
Data	1710	1740	1770	1780	1800	1820	1830	1860	1890

29. **(a)** $\mu = 240$, $\sigma = 12$
     (b) $Q_1 \approx 232$, $Q_3 \approx 248$
     (c)   From (b) we know that 50% of the time the number of heads will fall between 232 and 248 so bet (1) is the better bet.

According to the dishonest coin principle $\mu = 600 \times 0.4 = 240$ and $\sigma = \sqrt{600 \times 0.4 \times 0.6} = 12$.

	$\mu-3\sigma$	$\mu-2\sigma$	$\mu-\sigma$	$\mu-0.675\sigma$	μ	$\mu+0.675\sigma$	$\mu+\sigma$	$\mu+2\sigma$	$\mu+3\sigma$
Percentile	0.15	2.5	16	25	50	75	84	97.5	99.85
Data	204	216	228	232	240	248	252	264	278

31. **(a)** 20.55 pounds

The 95th percentile is approximately $17.25 + 1.65 \times 2 = 20.55$ pounds.

(b) 60th percentile

$17.75 = 17.25 + x \times 2$, so $x = 0.25$ and according to the table the child is in the 60th percentile.

(c) Slightly below the 16th percentile.

$17.25 - 15.2 = 2.05$, so the child is in slightly below the 16th percentile (since the 16th percentile is 1 standard deviation below the mean).